JUNIOR GREAT BOOKS

SERIES 8

◆   ◆   ◆

AN INTERPRETIVE READING, WRITING,

AND DISCUSSION CURRICULUM

JUNIOR GREAT BOOKS

SERIES 8

THE GREAT BOOKS FOUNDATION

A nonprofit educational corporation

First Printing

15   14   13   12   11

Printed in the United States of America

Published and distributed by

THE GREAT BOOKS FOUNDATION
A nonprofit educational corporation

35 East Wacker Drive, Suite 2300

Chicago, IL 60601-2298

CONTENTS

PREFACE

SHARED INQUIRY

In Junior Great Books you will explore a number of outstanding stories. You will do this in a variety of ways: by taking notes as you read, by looking at important words and passages, and by sharing your questions and ideas about each story with your group. In each of these activities, you and your classmates will be working together with your teacher or leader, asking and answering questions about what the story means. You will be sharing what you discover with your classmates. This way of reading, writing, and discussion in Junior Great Books is called *shared inquiry.*

One of the pleasures of shared inquiry is that you can speak without worrying about whether what you say is "the right answer." Different ideas and points of view can all lead to a better understanding of the story. When you speak, the leader may ask you to back up what you have said, or urge you to develop your idea further. Others in your class may also respond to what you say. They, too, may be asked to support their statements or explain them more clearly. After listening to what others say, you may change your mind about your answer. Shared inquiry gives you the chance to learn both from the author and from one another.

Sometimes you will focus on a small part of the story; at other times you will think about the story as a whole. As you participate in shared inquiry, you will develop your own *interpretation* of what you read—you will be working to discover what the author wants to tell you or make you feel through his or her words.

WHAT IS INTERPRETATION?

Good writers do their work with care. There are reasons for everything they put into their stories. They try to include only what has a point and what fits—things needed to make a story clear, to make it interesting, and to keep it moving along. They waste few words. In really good stories, everything fits. Everything has an explanation. The parts are connected and support one another just as the posts and beams in a building do.

The parts of the story, because they are connected, help to explain one another. Authors do not point out exactly how the parts are connected, nor do they say in so many words why everything in a story happens as it does. For one thing, that would make the story dull. For another, they want stories to be convincing—to seem like real life. In real life, few things that happen come complete with explanations. We have to puzzle out the explanations for ourselves.

Stories, too, ask us to work out many explanations for ourselves. And the answers to our questions are in the story, waiting to be found. Every good author puts into a story all that a reader must know to understand what is happening and why. As we figure out for ourselves why the things an author puts in a story are there, we are interpreting what we read. To interpret a story is to explain its meaning—what happens in it, and why, and what the story is about.

Some stories are simple and easy for us to understand. Others are more perplexing. In this second kind of story the author is trying to share with us ideas and feelings that are not obvious or easy to describe. You can fully understand such stories only if you actively seek their meaning out by asking questions.

ACTIVE READING

You will need to think hard about the stories you read in Junior Great Books—not just about *what* happens but also about *why* it happens the way it does. You will be reading each story at least twice. When you read a story for the first time, your mind is mainly on the action—on what the characters think, do, and say. As you read, the main question you ask is likely to be "What's going to happen next?" When you read a story for the second time, your mind will be free to raise new and different questions about it, and this will lead you to think of new questions to explore with your group. You will almost always notice details that you missed on your first reading, ones that can make you change your mind about why the characters behave as they do or how you feel about them. A second reading gives you the chance to think about the story as a whole without wondering what will happen next.

In shared inquiry, you will need to read with a pencil in hand and to make notes as you read. While you are reading, mark the words and passages in the story that strike you as really important, interesting, or surprising. Mark places that make you think of a question. Mark parts that give you ideas about what the story means. Your teacher or leader may also ask you to watch for particular things during your reading and to give them special attention. Your notes will remind you of your thoughts while reading and help you to find evidence to back up what you say.

As you read the stories in Junior Great Books, many questions will probably occur to you. In some cases your first reading of a story will give you the answer to these questions. But often after the first reading you may find that some of your questions haven't been answered. You will need to look actively for the answers when you read the story again. The second reading will help you bring these questions into focus and begin to look for possible answers to them.

Reading actively is reading with a purpose—to answer your questions about the story and to discover new questions. By reading with a purpose you will be able to draw on all parts of the text and think about what it means as a whole.

QUESTIONS OF FACT, INTERPRETATION, AND EVALUATION

There are three kinds of questions that can be asked about a story in Junior Great Books: questions of fact, questions of interpretation, and questions of evaluation. The examples of each given below are from "Sucker," the first story in this book.

Questions of fact ask you to recall particular details or events from a story. Everything the author puts into the story is a fact in that story, even if some of the things couldn't happen in real life. A question of fact has only one correct answer. Knowing and remembering the facts in a story is important. They are the basis for your opinions about the story's meaning. And you will use them to support your opinions.

Many times a leader will ask a factual question in order to get you to back up what you have said with evidence from the story. Suppose someone says, "Sucker is a lot younger than Pete." A leader might then ask, *How old are Sucker and Pete?* This question can be answered by pointing to the place in the story where Pete says that Sucker is "twelve, four years younger than I am." Pete himself must therefore be sixteen.

Now and then you will be asked a factual question that cannot be answered by looking at any one passage. For example, the question *Does Sucker forgive Pete for treating him badly?* can only be answered "No." Although the story does not come right out and say so, his behavior shows that he doesn't. Nothing in the story shows that Sucker does forgive Pete.

Questions of interpretation hold the central place in Junior Great Books. These are the questions that ask you to think carefully about what happens in a story and to consider what the story means. Unlike factual questions, they have more than a single good answer. Any answer that can be supported by factual evidence from the story will be a good one.

Some interpretive questions focus on a single passage or ask about a single event. Take, for example, this one: *Why does Pete want to tell Maybelle that Sucker is his kid brother?* One answer is that he wants Maybelle to know that he and Sucker are closer than cousins usually are. Another is that Pete is proud of Sucker, now that Sucker no longer looks "timid and sort of like he was afraid of a whack over the head." Still another answer is that Pete wants Maybelle to think of him as a mature "older brother."

Other, more basic interpretive questions are asked about the meaning of the story as a whole. The answers will often be drawn from several places in the story. Here is one basic interpretive question for "Sucker": *Why is the boys' room more Sucker's than Pete's at the end of the story?* To answer this question, you need to think about the various changes that occur in Pete, in Sucker, and in their relationship throughout the whole story.

Questions of evaluation ask how the story fits with your own experience and, after you have interpreted it, whether or not you agree with what the story is saying. As you read "Sucker," you might wonder *Do people like Sucker invite others to treat them badly?* In answering a question like this, you will be thinking more about yourself and your beliefs than about the story itself. After reading the story, thinking

vi

about evaluative questions can be a good way of deciding how you feel about the author's ideas.

Since understanding literature is the main purpose of Junior Great Books, you will spend most of your time considering questions of interpretation. Questions of fact will help you support your opinions about what a story means. Questions of evaluation will help you put yourself in the place of the characters in the story. You will have many chances to answer evaluative questions in your writing after Shared Inquiry Discussion.

SHARED INQUIRY DISCUSSION

After you have read a story twice, taken notes, and shared some of your questions with your classmates, you will be ready to participate in Shared Inquiry Discussion. Shared Inquiry Discussion begins when the discussion leader asks an interpretive question, a question that can have more than one good answer. The leader is not sure which answer is the best, and hopes to discover several good answers during the discussion. Because there can be more than one good answer, it takes many minds to discover and explore those answers fully. By asking questions, the leader seeks to help everyone in the group think for themselves about what the story means.

THE RULES OF SHARED INQUIRY DISCUSSION

1. **Only people who have read the story may take part in Shared Inquiry Discussion.** If you have not read the story, you cannot contribute to the discussion because you are unprepared to offer opinions and to support them with evidence from the story.

2. **Discuss only the story that everyone has read.** If you refer to other works of literature or your own personal experiences, the participants who are not familiar with them will not be able to contribute to the discussion. This rule also enables the group to check the validity of what is said by referring to the assigned story.

3. **Do not introduce outside opinions unless you can back them up with evidence of your own.** If you get an idea about the meaning of a story from an outside source—for example, the opinion of someone you know or an insight from another book—you may bring it up in discussion only if you can express it in your own words and support it with evidence from the story.

4. **Leaders may only ask questions; they may not answer them.** If leaders stated their own opinions about the meaning of a story, you might feel less inclined to think for yourself. You might also be less likely to believe that other equally good answers are possible. As a participant you are not limited to offering answers; you may ask questions, too.

In Shared Inquiry Discussion you may speak directly to anyone in the group, and not just to the leader. You may ask questions of anyone but the leader, and you will be answering questions that others ask you. Since you are all working together to search for a story's meaning, try to listen carefully when others are speaking. If you don't understand what they are saying, ask them to repeat their comments or explain them more clearly. If you disagree with what they are saying, you can tell them so, always giving your reasons. Sometimes, too, you will be able to support what another member of the group has said by giving a reason no one else has thought of.

By the end of a good discussion everyone in your group will understand the story better than they did before you began to exchange ideas, build on one another's insights, and work out new interpretations. At the close of a discussion, everyone will seldom agree in every detail on what the story means, but that's part of what makes it interesting and worthwhile to discuss the stories in Junior Great Books.

WRITING YOUR OWN INTERPRETIVE QUESTIONS

The more you participate in shared inquiry, the more you will see problems of meaning in the selections you read. Writing interpretive questions is one of the best ways to think on your own about the meaning of a story. Some of your notes may already be in the form of interpretive questions; others can be developed into questions.

The same responses that lead you to make notes on a story can be good sources of interpretive questions. Some of these sources are listed here, together with questions developed for "Sucker."

Look for words or passages that you think are important and that you wonder about. One reader was puzzled by Pete's statement, "I've sometimes thought that if we could have it out in a big fight that would help." He wrote this interpretive question:

Why does Pete feel that a big fight with Sucker might help to put things right between them?

Look for parts of the story that you feel strongly about. As you read a story, ask questions about whatever makes you react with strong feelings. Look for places where you agree or disagree with the characters or with the author. For instance, one reader felt strongly that Pete should have apologized to Sucker when he first realized that he had treated Sucker badly. She asked:

Why doesn't Pete apologize to Sucker, even though he realizes that the way he treated Sucker was "awful"?

When you are curious about why a character in the story acts the way he or she does, ask a question about that. One reader was curious about how Pete's feelings have changed at the end of the story and why he doesn't want to call his cousin "Sucker" anymore. He wrote:

Why doesn't Pete want to call Sucker by his nickname at the end of the story?

Let questions come out of your ideas about the meaning of the story. As you read, keep asking yourself what the author wants you to think about and experience through his or her words. Ask questions about that. One reader thought that the author, Carson McCullers, might be suggesting that Pete is not entirely to blame for what happens in his friendship with Sucker. She wrote:

Is the situation with Sucker all Pete's fault?

Interpretation begins with questions, the questions that come to you as you read. In working out the answers, you will arrive at a clearer idea of how the parts of the story fit together and have a better idea of its meaning.

SUCKER

Carson McCullers

It was always like I had a room to myself. Sucker slept in my bed with me but that didn't interfere with anything. The room was mine and I used it as I wanted to. Once I remember sawing a trap door in the floor. Last year when I was a sophomore in high school I tacked on my wall some pictures of girls from magazines and one of them was just in her underwear. My mother never bothered me because she had the younger kids to look after. And Sucker thought anything I did was always swell.

Whenever I would bring any of my friends back to my room all I had to do was just glance once at Sucker and he would get up from whatever he was busy with and maybe half smile at me, and leave without saying a word. He never brought kids back there. He's twelve, four years younger than I am, and he always knew without me even telling him that I didn't want kids that age meddling with my things.

Half the time I used to forget that Sucker isn't my brother. He's my first cousin but practically ever since I remember he's been in our family. You see his folks were killed in a wreck when he was a baby. To me and my kid sisters he was like our brother.

Sucker used to always remember and believe every word I said. That's how he got his nickname. Once a couple of years ago I told him that if he'd jump off our garage with an umbrella it would act as a parachute and he wouldn't fall hard. He did it and busted his knee. That's just one instance. And the funny thing was that no matter how many times he got fooled he would still believe me. Not that he was dumb in other ways—it was just the way he acted with me. He would look at everything I did and quietly take it in.

There is one thing I have learned, but it makes me feel guilty and is hard to figure out. If a person admires you a lot you despise him and don't care—and it is the person who doesn't notice you that you are apt to admire. This is not easy to realize. Maybelle Watts, this senior at school, acted like she was the Queen of Sheba and even humiliated me. Yet at this same time I would have done anything in the world to get her attentions. All I could think about day and night was Maybelle until I was nearly crazy. When Sucker was a little kid and on up until the time he was twelve I guess I treated him as bad as Maybelle did me.

Now that Sucker has changed so much it is a little hard to remember him as he used to be. I never imagined anything would suddenly happen that would make us both very different. I never knew that in order to get what has happened straight in my mind I would want to think back on him as he used to be and compare and try to get things settled. If I could have seen ahead maybe I would have acted different.

I never noticed him much or thought about him and when you consider how long we have had the same room together it is funny the few things I remember. He used to talk to himself a lot when he'd think he was alone—all about him fighting gangsters and being on ranches and that sort of kids' stuff. He'd get in the bathroom and stay as long as an hour and sometimes his voice would go up high and excited and you could hear him all over the house. Usually, though, he was very quiet. He didn't have many boys in the neighborhood to buddy with and his face had the look of a kid who is watching a game and waiting to be asked to play. He didn't mind wearing the sweaters and coats that I outgrew, even if the sleeves did flop down too big and make his wrists look as thin and white as a little girl's. That is how I remember him—getting a little bigger every year but still being the same. That was Sucker up until a few months ago when all this trouble began.

Maybelle was somehow mixed up in what happened so I guess I ought to start with her. Until I knew her I hadn't given much time to girls. Last fall she sat next to me in General Science class and that was when I first began to notice her. Her hair is the brightest yellow I ever saw and occasionally she will wear it set into curls with some sort of gluey stuff. Her fingernails are pointed and manicured and painted a shiny red. All during class I used to watch Maybelle, nearly all the time except when I thought she was going to look my way or when the teacher called on me. I couldn't keep my eyes off her hands, for one thing. They are very little and white except for that red stuff, and when she would turn the pages of her book she always licked her thumb and held out her little finger and turned very slowly. It is impossible to describe Maybelle. All the boys are crazy about her but she didn't even notice me. For one thing she's almost two years older than I am. Between periods I used to try and pass very close to her in the halls but she would hardly ever smile at me. All I could do was sit and

3

look at her in class—and sometimes it was like the whole room could hear my heart beating and I wanted to holler or light out and run for hell.

At night, in bed, I would imagine about Maybelle. Often this would keep me from sleeping until as late as one or two o'clock. Sometimes Sucker would wake up and ask me why I couldn't get settled and I'd tell him to hush his mouth. I suppose I was mean to him lots of times. I guess I wanted to ignore somebody like Maybelle did me. You could always tell by Sucker's face when his feelings were hurt. I don't remember all the ugly remarks I must have made because even when I was saying them my mind was on Maybelle.

That went on for nearly three months and then somehow she began to change. In the halls she would speak to me and every morning she copied my homework. At lunch time once I danced with her in the gym. One afternoon I got up nerve and went around to her house with a carton of cigarettes. I knew she smoked in the girls' basement and sometimes outside of school—and I didn't want to take her candy because I think that's been run into the ground. She was very nice and it seemed to me everything was going to change.

It was that night when this trouble really started. I had come into my room late and Sucker was already asleep. I felt too happy and keyed up to get in a comfortable position and I was awake thinking about Maybelle a long time. Then I dreamed about her and it seemed I kissed her. It was a surprise to wake up and see the dark. I lay still and a little while passed before I could come to and understand where I was. The house was quiet and it was a very dark night.

Sucker's voice was a shock to me. "Pete? . . ."

I didn't answer anything or even move.

"You do like me as much as if I was your own brother, don't you Pete?"

I couldn't get over the surprise of everything and it was like this was the real dream instead of the other.

"You have liked me all the time like I was your own brother, haven't you?"

"Sure," I said.

Then I got up for a few minutes. It was cold and I was glad to come back to bed. Sucker hung on to my back. He felt little and warm and I could feel his warm breathing on my shoulder.

"No matter what you did I always knew you liked me."

I was wide awake and my mind seemed mixed up in a strange way. There was this happiness about Maybelle and all that—but at the same time something about Sucker and his voice when he said these things made me take notice. Anyway I guess you understand people better when you are happy than when something is worrying you. It was like I had never really thought about Sucker until then. I felt I had always been mean to him. One night a few weeks before I had heard him crying in the dark. He said he had lost a boy's BB gun and was scared to let anybody know. He wanted me to tell him what to do. I was sleepy and tried to make him hush and when he wouldn't I kicked at him. That was just one of the things I remembered. It seemed to me he had always been a lonesome kid. I felt bad.

There is something about a dark cold night that makes you feel close to someone you're sleeping with. When you talk together it is like you are the only people awake in the town.

"You're a swell kid, Sucker," I said.

It seemed to me suddenly that I did like him more than anybody else I knew—more than any other boy, more than my sisters, more in a certain way even than Maybelle. I felt good all over and it was like when they play sad music in the movies. I wanted to show Sucker how much I really thought of him and make up for the way I had always treated him.

We talked for a good while that night. His voice was fast and it was like he had been saving up these things to tell me for a long time. He mentioned that he was going to try to build a canoe and that the kids down the block wouldn't let him in on their football team and I don't know what all. I talked some too and it was a good feeling to think of him taking in everything I said so seriously. I even spoke of Maybelle a little, only I made out like it was her who had been running after me all this time. He asked questions about high school and so forth. His voice was excited and he kept on talking fast like he could never get the words out in time. When I went to sleep he was still talking and I could still feel his breathing on my shoulder, warm and close.

During the next couple of weeks I saw a lot of Maybelle. She acted as though she really cared for me a little. Half the time I felt so good I hardly knew what to do with myself.

But I didn't forget about Sucker. There were a lot of old things in my bureau drawer I'd been saving—boxing gloves and Tom Swift books and second-rate fishing tackle. All this I turned over to him. We had some more talks together and it was really like I was knowing him for the first time. When there was a long cut on his cheek I knew he had been monkeying around with this new first razor set of mine, but I didn't say anything. His face seemed different now. He used to look timid and sort of like he was afraid of a whack over the head. That expression was gone. His face, with those wide-open eyes and his ears sticking out and his mouth never quite shut, had the look of a person who is surprised and expecting something swell.

Once I started to point him out to Maybelle and tell her he was my kid brother. It was an afternoon when a murder mystery was on at the movie. I had earned a dollar working for my dad and I gave Sucker a quarter to go and get candy and so forth. With the rest I took Maybelle. We were sitting near the back and I saw Sucker come in. He began to stare at the screen the minute he stepped past the ticket man and he stumbled down the aisle without noticing where he was going. I started to punch Maybelle but couldn't quite make up my mind. Sucker looked a little silly—walking like a drunk with his eyes glued to the movie. He was wiping his reading glasses on his shirttail and his knickers flopped down. He went on until he got to the first few rows where the kids usually sit. I never did punch Maybelle. But I got to thinking it was good to have both of them at the movie with the money I earned.

I guess things went on like this for about a month or six weeks. I felt so good I couldn't settle down to study or put my mind on anything. I wanted to be friendly with everybody. There were times when I just had to talk to some person. And usually that would be Sucker. He felt as good as I did. Once he said: "Pete, I am gladder that you are like my brother than anything else in the world."

Then something happened between Maybelle and me. I never have figured out just what it was. Girls like her are hard to understand. She began to act different toward me. At first I wouldn't let myself believe this and tried to think it was just my imagination. She didn't act glad to see me anymore. Often she went out riding with this fellow on the football team who owns this yellow roadster. The car was the color of her hair and after school she would ride off with him, laughing and looking into his face. I couldn't think of anything to do about it and she was on my mind all day and night. When I did get a chance to go out with her she was snippy and didn't seem to notice me. This made me feel like something was the matter—I would worry about my shoes clopping too loud on the floor, or the fly of my pants, or the bumps on my chin. Sometimes when Maybelle was around, a devil would get into me and I'd hold my face stiff and call grown men by their last names without the Mister and say rough things. In the night I would wonder what made me do all this until I was too tired for sleep.

At first I was so worried I just forgot about Sucker. Then later he began to get on my nerves. He was always hanging around until I would get back from high school, always looking like he had something to say to me or wanted me to tell him. He made me a magazine rack in his Manual Training class and one week he saved his lunch money and bought me three packs of cigarettes. He couldn't seem to take it in that I had things on my mind and didn't want to fool with him. Every afternoon it would be the same—him in my room with this waiting expression on his face. Then I wouldn't say anything or I'd maybe answer him rough-like and he would finally go on out.

I can't divide that time up and say this happened one day and that the next. For one thing I was so mixed up the weeks just slid along into each other and I felt like hell and didn't care. Nothing definite was said or done. Maybelle still rode around with this fellow in his yellow roadster and sometimes she would smile at me and sometimes not. Every afternoon I went from one place to another where I thought she would be. Either she would act almost nice and I would begin thinking how things would finally clear up and she would care for me—or else she'd behave so that if she hadn't been a girl I'd have wanted to grab her by that white little neck and choke her. The more ashamed I felt for making a fool of myself the more I ran after her.

Sucker kept getting on my nerves more and more. He would look at me as though he sort of blamed me for something, but at the same time knew that it wouldn't last long. He was growing fast and for some reason began to stutter when he talked. Sometimes he had nightmares or would throw up his breakfast. Mom got him a bottle of cod liver oil.

Then the finish came between Maybelle and me. I met her going to the drug store and asked for a date. When she said no I remarked something sarcastic. She told me she was sick and tired of my being around and that she had never cared a rap about me. She said all that. I just stood there and didn't answer anything. I walked home very slowly.

For several afternoons I stayed in my room by myself. I didn't want to go anywhere or talk to anyone. When Sucker would come in and look at me sort of funny I'd yell at him to get out. I didn't want to think of Maybelle and I sat at my desk reading *Popular Mechanics* or whittling at a toothbrush rack I was making. It seemed to me I was putting that girl out of my mind pretty well.

But you can't help what happens to you at night. That is what made things how they are now.

You see a few nights after Maybelle said those words to me I dreamed about her again. It was like that first time and I was squeezing Sucker's arm so tight I woke him up. He reached for my hand.

"Pete, what's the matter with you?"

All of a sudden I felt so mad my throat choked—at myself and the dream and Maybelle and Sucker and every single person I knew. I remembered all the times Maybelle had humiliated me and everything bad that had ever happened. It seemed to me for a second that nobody would ever like me but a sap like Sucker.

"Why is it we aren't buddies like we were before? Why—?"

"Shut your damn trap!" I threw off the cover and got up and turned on the light. He sat in the middle of the bed, his eyes blinking and scared.

There was something in me and I couldn't help myself. I don't think anybody ever gets that mad but once. Words came without me knowing what they would be. It was only afterward that I could remember each thing I said and see it all in a clear way.

"Why aren't we buddies? Because you're the dumbest slob I ever saw! Nobody cares anything about you! And just because I felt sorry for you sometimes and tried to act decent don't think I give a damn about a dumb-bunny like you!"

If I talked loud or hit him it wouldn't have been so bad. But my voice was slow and like I was very calm. Sucker's mouth was part way open and he looked as though he'd knocked his funny bone. His face was white and sweat came out on his forehead. He wiped it away with the back of his hand and for a minute his arm stayed raised that way as though he was holding something away from him.

"Don't you know a single thing? Haven't you ever been around at all? Why don't you get a girl friend instead of me? What kind of sissy do you want to grow up to be anyway?"

I didn't know what was coming next. I couldn't help myself or think.

Sucker didn't move. He had on one of my pajama jackets and his neck stuck out skinny and small. His hair was damp on his forehead.

"Why do you always hang around me? Don't you know when you're not wanted?"

Afterward I could remember the change in Sucker's face. Slowly that blank look went away and he closed his mouth. His eyes got narrow and his fists shut. There had never been such a look on him before. It was like every second he was getting older. There was a hard look to his eyes you don't see usually in a kid. A drop of sweat rolled down his chin and he didn't notice. He just sat there with those eyes on me and he didn't speak and his face was hard and didn't move.

"No you don't know when you're not wanted. You're too dumb. Just like your name—a dumb Sucker."

It was like something had busted inside me. I turned off the light and sat down in the chair by the window. My legs were shaking and I was so tired I could have bawled. The room was cold and dark. I sat there for a long time and smoked a squashed cigarette I had saved. Outside the yard was black and quiet. After a while I heard Sucker lie down.

I wasn't mad anymore, only tired. It seemed awful to me that I had talked like that to a kid only twelve. I couldn't take it all in. I told myself I would go over to him and try to make it up. But I just sat there in the cold until a long time had passed. I planned how I could straighten it out in the morning. Then, trying not to squeak the springs, I got back in bed.

Sucker was gone when I woke up the next day. And later when I wanted to apologize as I had planned he looked at me in this new hard way so that I couldn't say a word.

All of that was two or three months ago. Since then Sucker has grown faster than any boy I ever saw. He's almost as tall as I am and his bones have gotten heavier and bigger. He won't wear any of my old clothes anymore and has bought his first pair of long pants—with some leather suspenders to hold them up. Those are just the changes that are easy to see and put into words.

Our room isn't mine at all anymore. He's gotten up this gang of kids and they have a club. When they aren't digging trenches in some vacant lot and fighting they are always in

11

my room. On the door there is some foolishness written in Mercurochrome saying "Woe to the Outsider who Enters" and signed with crossed bones and their secret initials. They have rigged up a radio and every afternoon it blares out music. Once as I was coming in I heard a boy telling something in a low voice about what he saw in the back of his big brother's automobile. I could guess what I didn't hear. *That's what her and my brother do. It's the truth—parked in the car.* For a minute Sucker looked surprised and his face was almost like it used to be. Then he got hard and tough again. "Sure, dumbbell. We know all that." They didn't notice me. Sucker began telling them how in two years he was planning to be a trapper in Alaska.

But most of the time Sucker stays by himself. It is worse when we are alone together in the room. He sprawls across the bed in those long corduroy pants with the suspenders and just stares at me with that hard, half-sneering look. I fiddle around my desk and can't get settled because of those eyes of his. And the thing is I just have to study because I've gotten three bad cards this term already. If I flunk English I can't graduate next year. I don't want to be a bum and I just have to get my mind on it. I don't care a flip for Maybelle or any particular girl anymore and it's only this thing between Sucker and me that is the trouble now. We never speak except when we have to before the family. I don't even want to call him Sucker anymore and unless I forget I call him by his real name, Richard. At night I can't study with him in the room and I have to hang around the drug store, smoking and doing nothing, with the fellows who loaf there.

More than anything I want to be easy in my mind again. And I miss the way Sucker and I were for a while in a funny, sad way that before this I never would have believed. But everything is so different that there seems to be nothing I can do to get it right. I've sometimes thought if we could have it out in a big fight that would help. But I can't fight him because he's four years younger. And another thing— sometimes this look in his eyes makes me almost believe that if Sucker could he would kill me.

THE SUMMER OF THE BEAUTIFUL WHITE HORSE

William Saroyan

One day back there in the good old days when I was nine and the world was full of every imaginable kind of magnificence, and life was still a delightful and mysterious dream, my cousin Mourad, who was considered crazy by everybody who knew him except me, came to my house at four in the morning and woke me up by tapping on the window of my room.

Aram, he said.

I jumped out of bed and looked out the window.

I couldn't believe what I saw.

It wasn't morning yet, but it was summer and with daybreak not many minutes around the corner of the world it was light enough for me to know I wasn't dreaming.

My cousin Mourad was sitting on a beautiful white horse.

I stuck my head out of the window and rubbed my eyes.

Yes, he said in Armenian. It's a horse. You're not dreaming. Make it quick if you want to ride.

I knew my cousin Mourad enjoyed being alive more than

anybody else who had ever fallen into the world by mistake, but this was more than even I could believe.

In the first place, my earliest memories had been memories of horses and my first longings had been longings to ride.

This was the wonderful part.

In the second place, we were poor.

This was the part that wouldn't permit me to believe what I saw.

We were poor. We had no money. Our whole tribe was poverty-stricken. Every branch of the Garoghlanian family was living in the most amazing and comical poverty in the world. Nobody could understand where we ever got money enough to keep us with food in our bellies, not even the old men of the family. Most important of all, though, we were famous for our honesty. We had been famous for our honesty for something like eleven centuries, even when we had been the wealthiest family in what we liked to think was the world. We were proud first, honest next, and after that we believed in right and wrong. None of us would take advantage of anybody in the world, let alone steal.

Consequently, even though I could *see* the horse, so magnificent; even though I could *smell* it, so lovely; even though I could *hear* it breathing, so exciting; I couldn't *believe* the horse had anything to do with my cousin Mourad or with me or with any of the other members of our family, asleep or awake, because I *knew* my cousin Mourad couldn't have *bought* the horse, and if he couldn't have bought it he must have *stolen* it, and I refused to believe he had stolen it.

No member of the Garoghlanian family could be any kind of a thief, let alone a horse thief.

I stared first at my cousin and then at the horse. There was a pious stillness and humor in each of them which on the one hand delighted me and on the other frightened me.

Mourad, I said, where did you steal this horse?

Leap out of the window, he said, if you want to ride.

It was true, then. He *had* stolen the horse. There was no question about it. He had come to invite me to ride or not, as I chose.

Well, it seemed to me stealing a horse for a ride was not the same thing as stealing something else, such as money. For all I knew, maybe it wasn't stealing at all. If you were crazy about horses the way my cousin Mourad and I were, it wasn't stealing. It wouldn't become stealing until we offered to sell the horse, which of course I knew we would never do.

Let me put on some clothes, I said.

All right, he said, but hurry.

I leaped into my clothes.

I jumped down to the yard from the window and leaped up onto the horse behind my cousin Mourad.

That year we lived at the edge of town, on Walnut Avenue. Behind our house was the country: vineyards, orchards, irrigation ditches, and country roads. In less than three minutes we were on Olive Avenue, and then the horse began to trot. The air was new and lovely to breathe. The feel of the horse running was wonderful. My cousin Mourad, who was considered one of the craziest members of our family, began to sing. I mean, he began to roar.

Every family has a crazy streak in it somewhere, and my cousin Mourad was considered the natural inheritor of the crazy streak in our tribe. Before him was our uncle Khosrove, an enormous man with a powerful head of black hair and the largest mustache in the San Joaquin Valley, a man so furious in temper, so irritable, so impatient that he stopped anyone from talking by roaring, *It is no harm; pay no attention to it.*

That was all, no matter what anybody happened to be talking about. Once it was his own son Arak running eight

16

blocks to the barber shop where his father was having his mustache trimmed to tell him their house was on fire. This man Khosrove sat up in the chair and roared, It is no harm; pay no attention to it. The barber said, But the boy says your house is on fire. So Khosrove roared, Enough, it is no harm, I say.

My cousin Mourad was considered the descendant of this man, although Mourad's father was Zorab, who was practical and nothing else. That's how it was in our tribe. A man could be the father of his son's flesh, but that did not mean that he was also the father of his spirit. The distribution of the various kinds of spirit of our tribe had been from the beginning capricious and vagrant.

We rode and my cousin Mourad sang. For all anybody knew we were still in the old country where, at least according to some of our neighbors, we belonged. We let the horse run as long as it felt like running.

At last my cousin Mourad said, Get down. I want to ride alone.

Will you let me ride alone?

That is up to the horse.

The *horse* will let me ride.

We shall see. Don't forget that I have a way with a horse.

Well, any way you have with a horse, I have also.

For the sake of your safety, he said, let us hope so. Get down.

All right, I said, but remember you've got to let me try to ride alone.

I got down and my cousin Mourad kicked his heels into the horse and shouted, *Vazire*, run. The horse stood on its hind legs, snorted, and burst into a fury of speed that was the loveliest thing I had ever seen. My cousin Mourad raced the horse across a field of dry grass to an irrigation ditch, crossed the ditch on the horse, and five minutes later came back, dripping wet.

The sun was coming up, and so everything had bright light upon it, especially the horse.

Now it's my turn to ride, I said.

My cousin Mourad got off the horse.

Ride, he said.

I leaped to the back of the horse and for a moment knew the awfulest fear imaginable. The horse did not move.

Kick into his muscles, my cousin Mourad said. What are you waiting for? We've got to take him back before everybody in the world is up and about.

I kicked into the muscles of the horse. Once again it reared and snorted. Then it began to run. I didn't know what to do. Instead of running across the field to the irrigation ditch the horse ran down the road to the vineyard of Dikran Halabian where it began to leap over vines. The horse leaped over seven vines before I fell. Then it ran away.

My cousin Mourad came running down the road.

I'm not worried about you, he shouted. We've got to get that horse. You go this way and I'll go this way. If you come upon him, be kindly. I'll be near.

I ran down the road and my cousin Mourad ran across the field toward the irrigation ditch.

It took him half an hour to find the horse and bring him back.

All right, he said, jump on. The whole world is awake now.

What will we do? I said.

Well, he said, we'll either take him back or hide him until tomorrow morning.

He didn't sound worried and I knew he'd hide him and not take him back. Not for a while, at any rate.

Where will we hide him?

I know a place.

How long ago did you steal this horse? I said.

It suddenly dawned on me that he had been taking these early morning rides for some time and had come for me this morning only because he knew how much I longed to ride.

Who said anything about stealing a horse?

Anyhow, how long ago did you begin riding every morning?

Not until this morning.

Are you telling the truth?

Of course not, he said, but if we are found out, that's what you're to say. I don't want both of us to be liars. All you know is that we started riding this morning.

All right, I said.

He walked the horse quietly to the barn of a deserted vineyard which at one time had been the pride of a farmer named Vahan Fetvajian. There were some oats and dry alfalfa in the barn.

We began walking home.

It wasn't easy, he said, to get the horse to behave so nicely. At first it wanted to run wild, but, as I've told you, I have a way with a horse. I can get it to want to do anything *I* want it to do. Horses understand me.

How do you do it? I said.

I have an understanding with a horse.

Yes, but what kind of an understanding?

A simple and honest one.

Well, I wish I knew how to reach an understanding like that with a horse.

You're still a small boy, he said. When you get to be thirteen you'll know how to do it.

19

I went home and ate a hearty breakfast.

That afternoon my uncle Khosrove came to our house for coffee and cigarettes. He sat in the parlor, sipping and smoking and remembering the old country. Then another visitor arrived, a farmer named John Byro, an Assyrian who, out of loneliness, had learned to speak Armenian. My mother brought the lonely visitor coffee and tobacco and he rolled a cigarette and sipped and smoked, and then at last, sighing sadly, he said, My white horse which was stolen last month is still gone. I cannot understand it.

My uncle Khosrove became very irritated and shouted, It's no harm. What is the loss of a horse? Haven't we all lost the homeland? What is this crying over a horse?

That may be all right for you, a city dweller, to say, but what about my surrey? What good is a surrey without a horse?

Pay no attention to it, my uncle Khosrove roared.

I walked ten miles to get here.

You have legs.

My left leg pains me.

Pay no attention to it.

That horse cost me sixty dollars, John Byro said.

I spit on money, my uncle Khosrove said.

He got up and stalked out of the house, slamming the screen door.

My mother explained.

He has a gentle heart, she said. It is simply that he is home-sick and such a large man.

The farmer went away and I ran over to my cousin Mourad's house.

He was sitting under a peach tree, repairing the hurt wing of a young robin which could not fly. He was talking to the bird.

What is it? he said.

The farmer, John Byro. He visited our house. He wants his horse. You've had it a month. I want you to promise not to take it back until I learn to ride.

It will take you a *year* to learn to ride.

We could keep the horse a year.

My cousin Mourad leaped to his feet.

What? he roared. Are you inviting a member of the Garoghlanian family to steal? The horse must go back to its true owner.

When?

In six months at the latest.

He threw the bird into the air. The bird tried hard, almost fell twice, but at last flew away, high and straight.

Early every morning for two weeks my cousin Mourad and I took the horse out of the barn of the deserted vineyard where we were hiding it and rode it, and every morning the horse, when it was my turn to ride alone, leaped over grape vines and small trees and threw me and ran away. Nevertheless, I hoped in time to learn to ride the way my cousin Mourad rode.

One morning on our way to Vahan Fetvajian's deserted vineyard we ran into the farmer John Byro who was on his way to town.

Let me do the talking, my cousin Mourad said. I have a way with farmers.

Good morning, John Byro, my cousin Mourad said to the farmer.

The farmer studied the horse eagerly.

Good morning, sons of my friends, he said. What is the name of your horse?

My Heart, my cousin Mourad said in Armenian.

A lovely name for a lovely horse. I could swear it is the horse that was stolen from me many weeks ago. May I look into its mouth?

Of course, Mourad said.

The farmer looked into the mouth of the horse.

Tooth for tooth, he said. I would swear it *is* my horse if I didn't know your parents. The fame of your family for honesty is well known to me. Yet the horse is the twin of my horse. A suspicious man would believe his eyes instead of his heart. Good day, my young friends.

Good day, John Byro, my cousin Mourad said.

Early the following morning we took the horse to John Byro's vineyard and put it in the barn. The dogs followed us around without making a sound.

The dogs, I whispered to my cousin Mourad. I thought they would bark.

They would at somebody else, he said. I have a way with dogs.

My cousin Mourad put his arms around the horse, pressed his nose into the horse's nose, patted it, and then we went away.

That afternoon John Byro came to our house in his surrey and showed my mother the horse that had been stolen and returned.

I do not know what to think, he said. The horse is stronger than ever. Better-tempered, too. I thank God.

My uncle Khosrove, who was out of sight in the parlor, suddenly shouted. Quiet, man, quiet. Your horse has been returned. Pay no attention to it.

RULES OF THE GAME

Amy Tan

I was six when my mother taught me the art of invisible strength. It was a strategy for winning arguments, respect from others, and eventually, though neither of us knew it at the time, chess games.

"Bite back your tongue," scolded my mother when I cried loudly, yanking her hand toward the store that sold bags of salted plums. At home, she said, "Wise guy, he not go against wind. In Chinese we say, Come from South, blow with wind—poom!—North will follow. Strongest wind cannot be seen."

The next week I bit back my tongue as we entered the store with the forbidden candies. When my mother finished her shopping, she quietly plucked a small bag of plums from the rack and put it on the counter with the rest of the items.

My mother imparted her daily truths so she could help my older brothers and me rise above our circumstances. We lived in San Francisco's Chinatown. Like most of the other Chinese children who played in the back alleys of restaurants and curio shops, I didn't think we were poor. My bowl was always full, three five-course meals every day, beginning with a soup full of mysterious things I didn't want to know the names of.

We lived on Waverly Place, in a warm, clean, two-bedroom flat that sat above a small Chinese bakery specializing in steamed pastries and dim sum. In the early morning, when the alley was still quiet, I could smell fragrant red beans as they were cooked down to a pasty sweetness. By daybreak, our flat was heavy with the odor of fried sesame balls and sweet curried chicken crescents. From my bed, I would listen as my father got ready for work, then locked the door behind him, one-two-three clicks.

At the end of our two-block alley was a small sandlot playground with swings and slides well-shined down the middle with use. The play area was bordered by wood-slat benches where old-country people sat cracking roasted watermelon seeds with their golden teeth and scattering the husks to an impatient gathering of gurgling pigeons. The best playground, however, was the dark alley itself. It was crammed with daily mysteries and adventures. My brothers and I would peer into the medicinal herb shop, watching old Li dole out onto a stiff sheet of white paper the right amount of insect shells, saffron-colored seeds, and pungent leaves for his ailing customers. It was said that he once cured a woman dying of an ancestral curse that had eluded the best of American doctors. Next to the pharmacy was a printer who specialized in gold-embossed wedding invitations and festive red banners.

Farther down the street was Ping Yuen Fish Market. The front window displayed a tank crowded with doomed fish and turtles struggling to gain footing on the slimy green-tiled sides. A hand-written sign informed tourists, "Within this store, is all for food, not for pet." Inside, the butchers with their blood-stained white smocks deftly gutted the fish while customers cried out their orders and shouted, "Give me your freshest," to which the butchers always protested, "All are freshest." On less crowded market days, we would inspect the crates of live frogs and crabs which we were warned not to poke, boxes of dried cuttlefish, and row upon row of iced prawns, squid, and slippery fish. The sanddabs made me shiver each time; their eyes lay on one flattened side and reminded me of my mother's story of a careless girl who ran into a crowded street and was crushed by a cab. "Was smash flat," reported my mother.

At the corner of the alley was Hong Sing's, a four-table café with a recessed stairwell in front that led to a door marked "Tradesmen." My brothers and I believed the bad people emerged from this door at night. Tourists never went to Hong Sing's, since the menu was printed only in Chinese. A Caucasian man with a big camera once posed me and my playmates in front of the restaurant. He had us move to the side of the picture window so the photo would capture the roasted duck with its head dangling from a juice-covered rope. After he took the picture, I told him he should go into Hong Sing's and eat dinner. When he smiled and asked me what they served, I shouted, "Guts and duck's feet and octopus gizzards!" Then I ran off with my friends, shrieking with laughter as we scampered across the alley and hid in the entryway grotto of the China Gem Company, my heart pounding with hope that he would chase us.

My mother named me after the street that we lived on: Waverly Place Jong, my official name for important American documents. But my family called me Meimei, "Little Sister." I was the youngest, the only daughter. Each morning before school, my mother would twist and yank on my thick black

25

hair until she had formed two tightly wound pigtails. One day, as she struggled to weave a hard-toothed comb through my disobedient hair, I had a sly thought.

I asked her, "Ma, what is Chinese torture?" My mother shook her head. A bobby pin was wedged between her lips. She wetted her palm and smoothed the hair above my ear, then pushed the pin in so that it nicked sharply against my scalp.

"Who say this word?" she asked without a trace of knowing how wicked I was being. I shrugged my shoulders and said, "Some boy in my class said Chinese people do Chinese torture."

"Chinese people do many things," she said simply. "Chinese people do business, do medicine, do painting. Not lazy like American people. We do torture. Best torture."

My older brother Vincent was the one who actually got the chess set. We had gone to the annual Christmas party held at the First Chinese Baptist Church at the end of the alley. The missionary ladies had put together a Santa bag of gifts donated by members of another church. None of the gifts had names on them. There were separate sacks for boys and girls of different ages.

One of the Chinese parishioners had donned a Santa Claus costume and a stiff paper beard with cotton balls glued to it. I think the only children who thought he was the real thing were too young to know that Santa Claus was not Chinese. When my turn came up, the Santa man asked me how old I was. I thought it was a trick question; I was seven according to the American formula and eight by the Chinese calendar. I said I was born on March 17, 1951. That seemed to satisfy him. He then solemnly asked if I had been a very, very good girl this year and did I believe in Jesus Christ and obey my parents. I knew the only answer to that. I nodded back with equal solemnity.

Having watched the other children opening their gifts, I already knew that the big gifts were not necessarily the nicest ones. One girl my age got a large coloring book of biblical characters, while a less greedy girl who selected a smaller box received a glass vial of lavender toilet water. The sound of the box was also important. A ten-year-old boy had chosen a box that jangled when he shook it. It was a tin globe of the world with a slit for inserting money. He must have thought it was full of dimes and nickels, because when he saw that it had just ten pennies, his face fell with such undisguised disappointment that his mother slapped the side of his head and led him out of the church hall, apologizing to the crowd for her son who had such bad manners he couldn't appreciate such a fine gift.

As I peered into the sack, I quickly fingered the remaining presents, testing their weight, imagining what they contained. I chose a heavy, compact one that was wrapped in shiny silver foil and a red satin ribbon. It was a twelve-pack of Life Savers and I spent the rest of the party arranging and rearranging the candy tubes in the order of my favorites. My brother Winston chose wisely as well. His present turned out to be a box of intricate plastic parts; the instructions on the box proclaimed that when they were properly assembled he would have an authentic miniature replica of a World War II submarine.

Vincent got the chess set, which would have been a very decent present to get at a church Christmas party, except it was obviously used and, as we discovered later, it was missing a black pawn and a white knight. My mother graciously thanked the unknown benefactor, saying, "Too good. Cost too much." At which point, an old lady with fine white,

27

wispy hair nodded toward our family and said with a whistling whisper, "Merry, merry Christmas."

When we got home, my mother told Vincent to throw the chess set away. "She not want it. We not want it," she said, tossing her head stiffly to the side with a tight, proud smile. My brothers had deaf ears. They were already lining up the chess pieces and reading from the dog-eared instruction book.

I watched Vincent and Winston play during Christmas week. The chess board seemed to hold elaborate secrets waiting to be untangled. The chessmen were more powerful than Old Li's magic herbs that cured ancestral curses. And my brothers wore such serious faces that I was sure something was at stake that was greater than avoiding the tradesmen's door to Hong Sing's.

"Let me! Let me!" I begged between games when one brother or the other would sit back with a deep sigh of relief and victory, the other annoyed, unable to let go of the outcome. Vincent at first refused to let me play, but when I offered my Life Savers as replacements for the buttons that filled in for the missing pieces, he relented. He chose the flavors: wild cherry for the black pawn and peppermint for the white knight. Winner could eat both.

As our mother sprinkled flour and rolled out small doughy circles for the steamed dumplings that would be our dinner that night, Vincent explained the rules, pointing to each piece. "You have sixteen pieces and so do I. One king and queen, two bishops, two knights, two castles, and eight pawns. The pawns can only move forward one step, except on the first move. Then they can move two. But they can only take men by moving crossways like this, except in the beginning, when you can move ahead and take another pawn."

"Why?" I asked as I moved my pawn. "Why can't they move more steps?"

"Because they're pawns," he said.

"But why do they go crossways to take other men? Why aren't there any women and children?"

"Why is the sky blue? Why must you always ask stupid questions?" asked Vincent. "This is a game. These are the rules. I didn't make them up. See. Here. In the book." He jabbed a page with a pawn in his hand. "Pawn. P-A-W-N. Pawn. Read it yourself."

My mother patted the flour off her hands. "Let me see book," she said quietly. She scanned the pages quickly, not reading the foreign English symbols, seeming to search deliberately for nothing in particular.

"This American rules," she concluded at last. "Every time people come out from foreign country, must know rules. You not know, judge say, Too bad, go back. They not telling you why so you can use their way go forward. They say, Don't know why, you find out yourself. But they knowing all the time. Better you take it, find out why yourself." She tossed her head back with a satisfied smile.

I found out about all the whys later. I read the rules and looked up all the big words in a dictionary. I borrowed books from the Chinatown library. I studied each chess piece, trying to absorb the power each contained.

I learned about opening moves and why it's important to control the center early on; the shortest distance between two points is straight down the middle. I learned about the middle game and why tactics between two adversaries are like clashing ideas; the one who plays better has the clearest plans for both attacking and getting out of traps. I learned why it is essential in the endgame to have foresight, a mathematical understanding of all possible moves, and patience;

29

all weaknesses and advantages become evident to a strong adversary and are obscured to a tiring opponent. I discovered that for the whole game one must gather invisible strengths and see the endgame before the game begins.

I also found out why I should never reveal "why" to others. A little knowledge withheld is a great advantage one should store for future use. That is the power of chess. It is a game of secrets in which one must show and never tell.

I loved the secrets I found within the sixty-four black and white squares. I carefully drew a handmade chessboard and pinned it to the wall next to my bed, where at night I would stare for hours at imaginary battles. Soon I no longer lost any games or Life Savers, but I lost my adversaries. Winston and Vincent decided they were more interested in roaming the streets after school in their Hopalong Cassidy cowboy hats.

On a cold spring afternoon, while walking home from school, I detoured through the playground at the end of our alley. I saw a group of old men, two seated across a folding table playing a game of chess, others smoking pipes, eating peanuts, and watching. I ran home and grabbed Vincent's chess set, which was bound in a cardboard box with rubber bands. I also carefully selected two prized rolls of Life Savers. I came back to the park and approached a man who was observing the game.

"Want to play?" I asked him. His face widened with surprise and he grinned as he looked at the box under my arm.

"Little sister, been a long time since I play with dolls," he said, smiling benevolently. I quickly put the box down next to him on the bench and displayed my retort.

Lau Po, as he allowed me to call him, turned out to be a much better player than my brothers. I lost many games and many Life Savers. But over the weeks, with each diminishing roll of candies, I added new secrets. Lau Po gave me the names. The Double Attack from the East and West Shores. Throwing Stones on the Drowning Man. The Sudden Meeting of the Clan. The Surprise from the Sleeping Guard. The Humble Servant Who Kills the King. Sand in the Eyes of Advancing Forces. A Double Killing Without Blood.

There were also the fine points of chess etiquette. Keep captured men in neat rows, as well-tended prisoners. Never announce "Check" with vanity, lest someone with an unseen sword slit your throat. Never hurl pieces into the sandbox after you have lost a game, because then you must find them again, by yourself, after apologizing to all around you. By the end of the summer, Lau Po had taught me all he knew, and I had become a better chess player.

A small weekend crowd of Chinese people and tourists would gather as I played and defeated my opponents one by one. My mother would join the crowds during these outdoor exhibition games. She sat proudly on the bench, telling my admirers with proper Chinese humility, "Is luck."

A man who watched me play in the park suggested that my mother allow me to play in local chess tournaments. My mother smiled graciously, an answer that meant nothing. I desperately wanted to go, but I bit back my tongue. I knew she would not let me play among strangers. So as we walked home I said in a small voice that I didn't want to play in the local tournament. They would have American rules. If I lost, I would bring shame on my family.

"Is shame you fall down nobody push you," said my mother.

During my first tournament, my mother sat with me in the front row as I waited for my turn. I frequently bounced my legs to unstick them from the cold metal seat of the folding

31

chair. When my name was called, I leapt up. My mother unwrapped something in her lap. It was her *chang,* a small tablet of red jade which held the sun's fire. "Is luck," she whispered, and tucked it into my dress pocket. I turned to my opponent, a fifteen-year-old boy from Oakland. He looked at me, wrinkling his nose.

As I began to play, the boy disappeared, the color ran out of the room, and I saw only my white pieces and his black ones waiting on the other side. A light wind began blowing past my ears. It whispered secrets only I could hear.

"Blow from the South," it murmured. "The wind leaves no trail." I saw a clear path, the traps to avoid. The crowd rustled. "Shhh! Shhh!" said the corners of the room. The wind blew stronger. "Throw sand from the East to distract him." The knight came forward ready for the sacrifice. The wind hissed, louder and louder. "Blow, blow, blow. He cannot see. He is blind now. Make him lean away from the wind so he is easier to knock down."

"Check," I said, as the wind roared with laughter. The wind died down to little puffs, my own breath.

My mother placed my first trophy next to a new plastic chess set that the neighborhood Tao society had given to me. As she wiped each piece with a soft cloth, she said, "Next time win more, lose less."

"Ma, it's not how many pieces you lose," I said. "Some-times you need to lose pieces to get ahead."

"Better to lose less, see if you really need."

At the next tournament, I won again, but it was my mother who wore the triumphant grin.

"Lost eight piece this time. Last time was eleven. What I tell you? Better off lose less!" I was annoyed, but I couldn't say anything.

I attended more tournaments, each one farther away from home. I won all games, in all divisions. The Chinese bakery downstairs from our flat displayed my growing collection of trophies in its window, amidst the dust-covered cakes that were never picked up. The day after I won an important regional tournament, the window encased a fresh sheet cake with whipped-cream frosting and red script saying, "Congratulations, Waverly Jong, Chinatown Chess Champion." Soon after that, a flower shop, headstone engraver, and funeral parlor offered to sponsor me in national tournaments. That's when my mother decided I no longer had to do the dishes. Winston and Vincent had to do my chores.

"Why does she get to play and we do all the work," complained Vincent.

"Is new American rules," said my mother. "Meimei play, squeeze all her brains out for win chess. You play, worth squeeze towel."

By my ninth birthday, I was a national chess champion. I was still some 429 points away from grand-master status, but I was touted as the Great American Hope, a child prodigy and a girl to boot. They ran a photo of me in *Life* magazine next to a quote in which Bobby Fischer said, "There will never be a woman grand master." "Your move, Bobby," said the caption.

The day they took the magazine picture I wore neatly plaited braids clipped with plastic barrettes trimmed with rhinestones. I was playing in a large high school auditorium that echoed with phlegmy coughs and the squeaky rubber knobs of chair legs sliding across freshly waxed wooden floors. Seated across from me was an American man, about the same age as Lau Po, maybe fifty. I remember that his sweaty brow seemed to weep at my every move. He wore a dark, malodorous suit. One of his pockets was stuffed with a great white kerchief on which he wiped his palm before sweeping his hand over the chosen chess piece with great flourish.

In my crisp pink-and-white dress with scratchy lace at the neck, one of two my mother had sewn for these special occasions, I would clasp my hands under my chin, the delicate points of my elbows poised lightly on the table in the manner my mother had shown me for posing for the press. I would swing my patent leather shoes back and forth like an impatient child riding on a school bus. Then I would pause, suck in my lips, twirl my chosen piece in midair as if undecided, and then firmly plant it in its new threatening place, with a triumphant smile thrown back at my opponent for good measure.

I no longer played in the alley of Waverly Place. I never visited the playground where the pigeons and old men gathered. I went to school, then directly home to learn new chess secrets, cleverly concealed advantages, more escape routes.

But I found it difficult to concentrate at home. My mother had a habit of standing over me while I plotted out my games. I think she thought of herself as my protective ally. Her lips would be sealed tight, and after each move I made, a soft "Hmmmmph" would escape from her nose.

"Ma, I can't practice when you stand there like that," I said one day. She retreated to the kitchen and made loud noises with the pots and pans. When the crashing stopped, I could see out of the corner of my eye that she was standing in the doorway. "Hmmmph!" Only this one came out of her tight throat.

My parents made many concessions to allow me to practice. One time I complained that the bedroom I shared was so noisy that I couldn't think. Thereafter, my brothers slept in a bed in the living room facing the street. I said I couldn't finish my rice; my head didn't work right when my stomach was too full. I left the table with half-finished bowls and nobody complained. But there was one duty I couldn't avoid. I had to accompany my mother on Saturday market days when I had no tournament to play. My mother would proudly walk with me, visiting many shops, buying very little. "This my daughter Wave-ly Jong," she said to whoever looked her way.

One day, after we left a shop I said under my breath, "I wish you wouldn't do that, telling everybody I'm your daughter." My mother stopped walking. Crowds of people with heavy bags pushed past us on the sidewalk, bumping into first one shoulder, then another.

"Aiii-ya. So shame be with mother?" She grasped my hand even tighter as she glared at me.

I looked down. "It's not that, it's just so obvious. It's just so embarrassing."

"Embarrass you be my daughter?" Her voice was cracking with anger.

"That's not what I meant. That's not what I said."

"What you say?"

I knew it was a mistake to say anything more, but I heard my voice speaking. "Why do you have to use me to show off? If you want to show off, then why don't you learn to play chess."

My mother's eyes turned into dangerous black slits. She had no words for me, just sharp silence.

I felt the wind rushing around my hot ears. I jerked my hand out of my mother's tight grasp and spun around, knocking into an old woman. Her bag of groceries spilled to the ground.

"Aii-ya! Stupid girl!" my mother and the woman cried. Oranges and tin cans careened down the sidewalk. As my mother stooped to help the old woman pick up the escaping food, I took off.

I raced down the street, dashing between people, not looking back as my mother screamed shrilly, "Meimei! Meimei!" I fled down an alley, past dark curtained shops and merchants washing the grime off their windows. I sped into the sunlight, into a large street crowded with tourists examining trinkets and souvenirs. I ducked into another dark alley, down another street, up another alley. I ran until it hurt and I realized I had nowhere to go, that I was not running from anything. The alleys contained no escape routes.

My breath came out like angry smoke. It was cold. I sat down on an upturned plastic pail next to a stack of empty boxes, cupping my chin with my hands, thinking hard. I imagined my mother, first walking briskly down one street or another looking for me, then giving up and returning home to await my arrival. After two hours, I stood up on creaking legs and slowly walked home.

The alley was quiet and I could see the yellow lights shining from our flat like two tiger's eyes in the night. I climbed the sixteen steps to the door, advancing quietly up each so as not to make any warning sounds. I turned the knob; the door was locked. I heard a chair moving, quick steps, the locks turning—click! click! click!—and then the door opened.

"About time you got home," said Vincent. "Boy, are you in trouble."

He slid back to the dinner table. On a platter were the remains of a large fish, its fleshy head still connected to bones swimming upstream in vain escape. Standing there waiting for my punishment, I heard my mother speak in a dry voice.

36

"We not concerning this girl. This girl not have concerning for us."

Nobody looked at me. Bone chopsticks clinked against the insides of bowls being emptied into hungry mouths.

I walked into my room, closed the door, and lay down on my bed. The room was dark, the ceiling filled with shadows from the dinnertime lights of neighboring flats.

In my head, I saw a chessboard with sixty-four black and white squares. Opposite me was my opponent, two angry black slits. She wore a triumphant smile. "Strongest wind cannot be seen," she said.

Her black men advanced across the plane, slowly marching to each successive level as a single unit. My white pieces screamed as they scurried and fell off the board one by one. As her men drew closer to my edge, I felt myself growing light. I rose up into the air and flew out the window. Higher and higher, above the alley, over the tops of tiled roofs, where I was gathered up by the wind and pushed up toward the night sky until everything below me disappeared and I was alone.

I closed my eyes and pondered my next move.

THE DESTRUCTORS

Graham Greene

1

It was on the eve of August Bank Holiday that the latest recruit became the leader of the Wormsley Common Gang. No one was surprised except Mike, but Mike at the age of nine was surprised by everything. "If you don't shut your mouth," somebody once said to him, "you'll get a frog down it." After that Mike kept his teeth tightly clamped except when the surprise was too great.

The new recruit had been with the gang since the beginning of the summer holidays, and there were possibilities about his brooding silence that all recognized. He never wasted a word even to tell his name until that was required of him by the rules. When he said "Trevor" it was a statement of fact, not as it would have been with the others a statement of shame or defiance. Nor did anyone laugh except Mike, who, finding himself without support, and meeting the dark gaze of the newcomer, opened his mouth and was quiet again. There was every reason why T., as he was afterwards referred to, should have been an object of mockery—there was his name (and they substituted the initial because otherwise they had no excuse not to laugh at it), the fact that his father, a former architect and present clerk, had "come down in the world" and that his mother considered herself better than the neighbours. What but an odd quality of danger, of the unpredictable, established him in the gang without any ignoble ceremony of initiation?

The gang met every morning in an impromptu car-park, the site of the last bomb of the first blitz. The leader, who was known as Blackie, claimed to have heard it fall, and no one was precise enough in his dates to point out that he would have been one year old and fast asleep on the down platform of Wormsley Common Underground Station. On one side of the car-park leant the first occupied house, No. 3, of the shattered Northwood Terrace—literally leant, for it had suffered from the blast of the bomb and the side walls were supported on wooden struts. A smaller bomb and some incendiaries had fallen beyond, so that the house stuck up like a jagged tooth and carried on the further wall relics of its neighbour, a dado, the remains of a fireplace. T., whose words were almost confined to voting "Yes" or "No" to the plan of operations proposed each day by Blackie, once startled the whole gang by saying broodingly, "Wren* built that house, father says."

"Who's Wren?"

"The man who built St. Paul's."

"Who cares?" Blackie said. "It's only Old Misery's."

Old Misery—whose real name was Thomas—had once been a builder and decorator. He lived alone in the crippled house, doing for himself: once a week you could see him

---

* **Wren.** Sir Christopher Wren (1632-1723), the greatest English architect of his time, was instrumental in rebuilding London after the Great Fire of 1666. St. Paul's Cathedral is his masterpiece.

coming back across the common with bread and vegetables, and once as the boys played in the car-park he put his head over the smashed wall of his garden and looked at them.

"Been to the lav," one of the boys said, for it was common knowledge that since the bombs fell something had gone wrong with the pipes of the house and Old Misery was too mean to spend money on the property. He could do the redecorating himself at cost price, but he had never learnt plumbing. The lav was a wooden shed at the bottom of the narrow garden with a star-shaped hole in the door: it had escaped the blast which had smashed the house next door and sucked out the window-frames of No. 3.

The next time the gang became aware of Mr. Thomas was more surprising. Blackie, Mike, and a thin yellow boy, who for some reason was called by his surname Summers, met him on the common coming back from the market. Mr. Thomas stopped them. He said glumly, "You belong to the lot that play in the car-park?"

Mike was about to answer when Blackie stopped him. As the leader he had responsibilities. "Suppose we are?" he said ambiguously.

"I got some chocolates," Mr. Thomas said. "Don't like 'em myself. Here you are. Not enough to go round, I don't suppose. There never is," he added with sombre conviction. He handed over three packets of Smarties.

The gang was puzzled and perturbed by this action and tried to explain it away. "Bet someone dropped them and he picked 'em up," somebody suggested.

"Pinched 'em and then got in a bleeding funk," another thought aloud.

"It's a bribe," Summers said. "He wants us to stop bouncing balls on his wall."

"We'll show him we don't take bribes," Blackie said, and

they sacrificed the whole morning to the game of bouncing that only Mike was young enough to enjoy. There was no sign from Mr. Thomas. — *stop*

Next day T. astonished them all. He was late at the ren-dezvous, and the voting for that day's exploit took place without him. At Blackie's suggestion the gang was to disperse in pairs, take buses at random, and see how many free rides could be snatched from unwary conductors (the operation was to be carried out in pairs to avoid cheating). They were drawing lots for their companions when T. arrived.

"Where you been, T.?" Blackie asked. "You can't vote now. You know the rules."

"I've been *there,*" T. said. He looked at the ground, as though he had thoughts to hide.

"Where?"

"At Old Misery's." Mike's mouth opened and then hur-riedly closed again with a click. He had remembered the frog.

"At Old Misery's?" Blackie said. There was nothing in the rules against it, but he had a sensation that T. was treading on dangerous ground. He asked hopefully, "Did you break in?"

"No. I rang the bell."

"And what did you say?"

"I said I wanted to see his house."

"What did he do?"

"He showed it me."

"Pinch anything?"

"No."

"What did you do it for then?"

The gang had gathered round: it was as though an impromptu court were about to form and try some case of deviation. T. said, "It's a beautiful house," and still watching the ground, meeting no one's eyes, he licked his lips first one way, then the other.

"What do you mean, a beautiful house?" Blackie asked with scorn.

"It's got a staircase two hundred years old like a corkscrew. Nothing holds it up."

"What do you mean, nothing holds it up. Does it float?"

"It's to do with opposite forces, Old Misery said."

"What else?"

"There's panelling."

"Like in the Blue Boar?"

"Two hundred years old."

"Is Old Misery two hundred years old?"

Mike laughed suddenly and then was quiet again. The meeting was in a serious mood. For the first time since T. had strolled into the car-park on the first day of the holidays, his position was in danger. It only needed a single use of his real name and the gang would be at his heels.

"What did you do it for?" Blackie asked. He was just, he had no jealousy, he was anxious to retain T. in the gang if he could. It was the word "beautiful" that worried him—that belonged to a class world that you could still see parodied at the Wormsley Common Empire by a man wearing a top hat and a monocle, with a haw-haw accent. He was tempted to say, "My dear Trevor, old chap," and unleash his hell hounds. "If you'd broken in," he said sadly—that indeed would have been an exploit worthy of the gang.

"This was better," T. said. "I found out things." He continued to stare at his feet, not meeting anybody's eye, as though he were absorbed in some dream he was unwilling—or ashamed—to share.

"What things?"

"Old Misery's going to be away all tomorrow and Bank Holiday."

Blackie said with relief, "You mean we could break in?"

"And pinch things?" somebody asked.

Blackie said, "Nobody's going to pinch things. Breaking in—that's good enough, isn't it? We don't want any court stuff."

"I don't want to pinch anything," T. said. "I've got a better idea."

"What is it?"

T. raised eyes as grey and disturbed as the drab August day. "We'll pull it down," he said. "We'll destroy it."

Blackie gave a single hoot of laughter and then, like Mike, fell quiet, daunted by the serious implacable gaze. "What'd the police be doing all the time?" he said.

"They'd never know. We'd do it from inside. I've found a way in." He said with a sort of intensity, "We'd be like worms, don't you see, in an apple. When we came out again there'd be nothing there, no staircase, no panels, nothing but just walls, and then we'd make the walls fall down—somehow."

"We'd go to jug," Blackie said.

"Who's to prove? and anyway we wouldn't have pinched anything." He added without the smallest flicker of glee, "There wouldn't be anything to pinch after we'd finished."

"I've never heard of going to prison for breaking things," Summers said.

"There wouldn't be time," Blackie said. "I've seen house-breakers at work."

"There are twelve of us," T. said. "We'd organize."

"None of us know how . . ."

"I know," T. said. He looked across at Blackie. "Have you got a better plan?"

"Today," Mike said tactlessly, "we're pinching free rides . . ."

"Free rides," T. said. "Kid stuff. You can stand down, Blackie, if you'd rather . . ."

"The gang's got to vote."

43

"Put it up then."

Blackie said uneasily, "It's proposed that tomorrow and Monday we destroy Old Misery's house."

"Here, here," said a fat boy called Joe.

"Who's in favour?"

T. said, "It's carried."

"How do we start?" Summers asked.

"He'll tell you," Blackie said. It was the end of his leadership. He went away to the back of the car-park and began to kick a stone, dribbling it this way and that. There was only one old Morris in the park, for few cars were left there except lorries: without an attendant there was no safety. He took a flying kick at the car and scraped a little paint off the rear mudguard. Beyond, paying no more attention to him than to a stranger, the gang had gathered round T.; Blackie was dimly aware of the fickleness of favour. He thought of going home, of never returning, of letting them all discover the hollowness of T.'s leadership, but suppose after all what T. proposed was possible—nothing like it had ever been done before. The fame of the Wormsley Common car-park gang would surely reach around London. There would be headlines in the papers. Even the grown-up gangs who ran the betting at the all-in wrestling and the barrow-boys would hear with respect of how Old Misery's house had been destroyed. Driven by the pure, simple, and altruistic ambition of fame for the gang, Blackie came back to where T. stood in the shadow of Old Misery's wall.

T. was giving his orders with decision: it was as though this plan had been with him all his life, pondered through the seasons, now in his fifteenth year crystallized with the pain of puberty. "You," he said to Mike, "bring some big nails, the biggest you can find, and a hammer. Anybody who can, better bring a hammer and a screwdriver. We'll need plenty of them. Chisels too. We can't have too many chisels. Can anybody bring a saw?"

"I can," Mike said.

"Not a child's saw," T. said. "A real saw."

Blackie realized he had raised his hand like any ordinary member of the gang.

"Right, you bring one, Blackie. But now there's a difficulty. We want a hacksaw."

"What's a hacksaw?" someone asked.

"You can get 'em at Woolworth's," Summers said.

The fat boy called Joe said gloomily, "I knew it would end in a collection."

"I'll get one myself," T. said. "I don't want your money. But I can't buy a sledge-hammer."

Blackie said, "They are working on No. 15. I know where they'll leave their stuff for Bank Holiday."

"Then that's all," T. said. "We meet here at nine sharp."

"I've got to go to church," Mike said.

"Come over the wall and whistle. We'll let you in."

2

On Sunday morning all were punctual except Blackie, even Mike. Mike had a stroke of luck. His mother felt ill, his father was tired after Saturday night, and he was told to go to church alone with many warnings of what would happen if he strayed. Blackie had difficulty in smuggling out the saw, and then in finding the sledge-hammer at the back of No. 15. He approached the house from a lane at the rear of the garden, for fear of the policeman's beat along the main road. The tired evergreens kept off a stormy sun: another wet Bank Holiday was being prepared over the Atlantic, beginning in swirls of dust under the trees. Blackie climbed the wall into Misery's garden.

There was no sign of anybody anywhere. The lav stood like a tomb in a neglected graveyard. The curtains were drawn. The house slept. Blackie lumbered nearer with the saw and the sledge-hammer. Perhaps after all nobody had turned up: the plan had been a wild invention: they had woken wiser. But when he came close to the back door he could hear a confusion of sound hardly louder than a hive in swarm: a clickety-clack, a bang bang, a scraping, a creaking, a sudden painful crack. He thought: it's true, and whistled.

They opened the back door to him and he came in. He had at once the impression of organization, very different from the old happy-go-lucky ways under his leadership. For a while he wandered up and down stairs looking for T. Nobody addressed him: he had a sense of great urgency, and already he could begin to see the plan. The interior of the house was being carefully demolished without touching the outer walls. Summers with hammer and chisel was ripping out the skirting-boards in the ground floor dining room: he had already smashed the panels of the door. In the same room Joe was heaving up the parquet blocks, exposing the soft wood floorboards over the cellar. Coils of wire came out of the damaged skirting and Mike sat happily on the floor clipping the wires.

On the curved stairs two of the gang were working hard with an inadequate child's saw on the banisters—when they saw Blackie's big saw they signalled for it wordlessly. When he next saw them a quarter of the banisters had been dropped into the hall. He found T. at last in the bathroom—he sat moodily in the least cared-for room in the house, listening to the sounds coming up from below.

"You've really done it," Blackie said with awe. "What's going to happen?"

"We've only just begun," T. said. He looked at the sledge-hammer and gave his instructions. "You stay here and break the bath and wash-basin. Don't bother about the pipes. They come later."

Mike appeared at the door. "I've finished the wires, T.," he said.

"Good. You've just got to go wandering round now. The kitchen's in the basement. Smash all the china and glass and bottles you can lay hold of. Don't turn on the taps—we don't want a flood—yet. Then go into all the rooms and turn out drawers. If they are locked get one of the others to break them open. Tear up any papers you find and smash all the orna-ments. Better take a carving-knife with you from the kitchen. The bedroom's opposite here. Open the pillows and tear up the sheets. That's enough for the moment. And you, Blackie, when you've finished in here crack the plaster in the passage up with your sledge-hammer."

"What are you going to do?" Blackie asked.

"I'm looking for something special," T. said.

It was nearly lunchtime before Blackie had finished and went in search of T. Chaos had advanced. The kitchen was a shambles of broken glass and china. The dining room was stripped of parquet, the skirting was up, the door had been taken off its hinges, and the destroyers had moved up a floor. Streaks of light came in through the closed shutters where they worked with the seriousness of creators—and destruction after all is a form of creation. A kind of imagination had seen this house as it had now become.

Mike said, "I've got to go home for dinner."

"Who else?" T. asked, but all the others on one excuse or another had brought provisions with them.

They squatted in the ruins of the room and swapped unwanted sandwiches. Half an hour for lunch and they were

47

at work again. By the time Mike returned they were on the top floor, and by six the superficial damage was completed. The doors were all off, all the skirtings raised, the furniture pillaged and ripped and smashed—no one could have slept in the house except on a bed of broken plaster. T. gave his orders—eight o'clock next morning—and to escape notice they climbed singly over the garden wall, into the car-park. Only Blackie and T. were left: the light had nearly gone, and when they touched a switch, nothing worked—Mike had done his job thoroughly.

"Did you find anything special?" Blackie asked.

T. nodded. "Come over here," he said, "and look." Out of both pockets he drew bundles of pound notes. "Old Misery's savings," he said. "Mike ripped out the mattress, but he missed them."

"What are you going to do? Share them?"

"We aren't thieves," T. said. "Nobody's going to steal anything from this house. I kept these for you and me—a celebration." He knelt down on the floor and counted them out—there were seventy in all. "We'll burn them," he said, "one by one," and taking it in turns they held a note upwards and lit the top corner, so that the flame burnt slowly towards their fingers. The grey ash floated above them and fell on their heads like age. "I'd like to see Old Misery's face when we are through," T. said.

"You hate him a lot?" Blackie asked.

"Of course I don't hate him," T. said. "There'd be no fun if I hated him." The last burning note illuminated his brooding face. "All this hate and love," he said, "it's soft, it's hooey. There's only things, Blackie," and he looked round the room crowded with the unfamiliar shadows of half-things, broken things, former things. "I'll race you home, Blackie," he said.

Next morning the serious destruction started. Two were missing—Mike and another boy whose parents were off to Southend and Brighton in spite of the slow warm drops that had begun to fall and the rumble of thunder in the estuary like the first guns of the old blitz. "We've got to hurry," T. said.

Summers was restive. "Haven't we done enough?" he asked. "I've been given a bob for slot machines. This is like work."

"We've hardly started," T. said. "Why, there's all the floors left, and the stairs. We haven't taken out a single window. You voted like the others. We are going to *destroy* this house. There won't be anything left when we've finished."

They began again on the first floor picking up the top floor-boards next the outer wall, leaving the joists exposed. Then they sawed through the joists and retreated into the hall, as what was left of the floor heeled and sank. They had learnt with practice, and the second floor collapsed more easily. By the evening an odd exhilaration seized them as they looked down the great hollow of the house. They ran risks and made mistakes: when they thought of the windows it was too late to reach them. "Cor," Joe said, and dropped a penny down into the dry rubble-filled well. It cracked and spun amongst the broken glass.

"Why did we start this?" Summers asked with astonishment; T. was already on the ground, digging at the rubble, clearing a space along the outer wall. "Turn on the taps," he said. "It's too dark for anyone to see now, and in the morning it won't matter." The water overtook them on the stairs and fell through the floorless rooms.

It was then they heard Mike's whistle at the back. "Something's wrong," Blackie said. They could hear his urgent breathing as they unlocked the door.

"The bogies?" Summers asked.

"Old Misery," Mike said. "He's on his way." He put his head between his knees and retched. "Ran all the way," he said with pride.

"But why?" T. said. "He told me . . ." He protested with the fury of the child he had never been, "It isn't fair."

"He was down at Southend," Mike said, "and he was on the train coming back. Said it was too cold and wet." He paused and gazed at the water. "My, you've had a storm here. Is the roof leaking?"

"How long will he be?"

"Five minutes. I gave Ma the slip and ran."

"We better clear," Summers said. "We've done enough, anyway."

"Oh no, we haven't. Anybody could do this—" "this" was the shattered hollowed house with nothing left but the walls. Yet walls could be preserved. Facades were valuable. They could build inside again more beautifully than before. This could again be a home. He said angrily, "We've got to finish. Don't move. Let me think."

"There's no time," a boy said.

"There's got to be a way," T. said. "We couldn't have got this far . . ."

"We've done a lot," Blackie said.

"No. No, we haven't. Somebody watch the front."

"We can't do any more."

"He may come in at the back."

"Watch the back too." T. began to plead. "Just give me a minute and I'll fix it. I swear I'll fix it." But his authority had gone with his ambiguity. He was only one of the gang. "Please," he said.

"Please," Summers mimicked him, and then suddenly struck home with the fatal name. "Run along home, Trevor."

T. stood with his back to the rubble like a boxer knocked groggy against the ropes. He had no words as his dreams shook and slid. Then Blackie acted before the gang had time to laugh, pushing Summers backward. "I'll watch the front, T.," he said, and cautiously he opened the shutters of the hall. The grey wet common stretched ahead, and the lamps gleamed in the puddles. "Someone's coming, T. No, it's not him. What's your plan, T.?"

"Tell Mike to go out to the lav and hide close beside it. When he hears me whistle he's got to count ten and start to shout."

"Shout what?"

"Oh, 'Help,' anything."

"You hear, Mike," Blackie said. He was the leader again. He took a quick look between the shutters. "He's coming, T."

"Quick, Mike. The lav. Stay here, Blackie, all of you, till I yell."

"Where are you going, T.?"

"Don't worry. I'll see to this. I said I would, didn't I?"

Old Misery came limping off the common. He had mud on his shoes and he stopped to scrape them on the pavement's edge. He didn't want to soil his house, which stood jagged and dark between the bomb-sites, saved so narrowly, as he believed, from destruction. Even the fanlight had been left unbroken by the bomb's blast. Somewhere somebody whistled. Old Misery looked sharply round. He didn't trust whistles. A child was shouting: it seemed to come from his own garden. Then a boy ran into the road from the car-park. "Mr. Thomas," he called, "Mr. Thomas."

"What is it?"

"I'm terribly sorry, Mr. Thomas. One of us got taken short, and we thought you wouldn't mind, and now he can't get out."

"What do you mean, boy?"

"He's got stuck in your lav."

"He'd no business . . . Haven't I seen you before?"

"You showed me your house."

"So I did. So I did. That doesn't give you the right to . . ."

"Do hurry, Mr. Thomas. He'll suffocate."

"Nonsense. He can't suffocate. Wait till I put my bag in."

"I'll carry your bag."

"Oh no, you don't. I carry my own."

"This way, Mr. Thomas."

"I can't get in the garden that way. I've got to go through the house."

"But you *can* get in the garden this way, Mr. Thomas. We often do."

"You often do?" He followed the boy with a scandalized fascination. "When? What right . . . ?"

"Do you see . . . ? the wall's low."

"I'm not going to climb walls into my own garden. It's absurd."

"This is how we do it. One foot here, one foot there, and over." The boy's face peered down, an arm shot out, and Mr. Thomas found his bag taken and deposited on the other side of the wall.

"Give me back my bag," Mr. Thomas said. From the loo a boy yelled and yelled. "I'll call the police."

"Your bag's all right, Mr. Thomas. Look. One foot there. On your right. Now just above. To your left." Mr. Thomas climbed over his own garden wall. "Here's your bag, Mr. Thomas."

"I'll have the wall built up," Mr. Thomas said, "I'll not have you boys coming over here, using my loo." He stumbled on the path, but the boy caught his elbow and supported him. "Thank you, thank you, my boy," he murmured automatically. Somebody shouted again through the dark. "I'm coming, I'm coming," Mr. Thomas called. He said to the boy beside him, "I'm not unreasonable. Been a boy myself. As long as things are done regular. I don't mind you playing round the place Saturday mornings. Sometimes I like company. Only it's got to be regular. One of you asks leave and I say Yes. Sometimes I'll say No. Won't feel like it. And you come in at the front door and out at the back. No garden walls."

"Do get him out, Mr. Thomas."

"He won't come to any harm in my loo," Mr. Thomas said, stumbling slowly down the garden. "Oh, my rheumatics," he said. "Always get 'em on Bank Holiday. I've got to go careful. There's loose stones here. Give me your hand. Do you know what my horoscope said yesterday? 'Abstain from any dealings in first half of week. Danger of serious crash.' That might be on this path," Mr. Thomas said. "They speak in parables and double meanings." He paused at the door of the loo. "What's the matter in there?" he called. There was no reply.

"Perhaps he's fainted," the boy said.

"Not in my loo. Here, you, come out," Mr. Thomas said, and giving a great jerk at the door he nearly fell on his back when it swung easily open. A hand first supported him and then pushed him hard. His head hit the opposite wall and he sat heavily down. His bag hit his feet. A hand whipped the key out of the lock and the door slammed. "Let me out," he called, and heard the key turn in the lock. "A serious crash," he thought, and felt dithery and confused and old.

A voice spoke to him softly through the star-shaped hole in the door. "Don't worry, Mr. Thomas," it said, "we won't hurt you, not if you stay quiet."

Mr. Thomas put his head between his hands and pondered. He had noticed that there was only one lorry in the car-park, and he felt certain that the driver would not come for it before the morning. Nobody could hear him from the road in front, and the lane at the back was seldom used. Anyone who passed there would be hurrying home and would not pause for what they would certainly take to be drunken cries. And if he did call "Help," who, on a lonely Bank Holiday evening, would have the courage to investigate? Mr. Thomas sat on the loo and pondered with the wisdom of age.

After a while it seemed to him that there were sounds in the silence—they were faint and came from the direction of his house. He stood up and peered through the ventilation-hole—between the cracks in one of the shutters he saw a light, not the light of a lamp, but the wavering light that a candle might give. Then he thought he heard the sound of hammering and scraping and chipping. He thought of burglars—perhaps they had employed the boy as a scout, but why should burglars engage in what sounded more and more like a stealthy form of carpentry? Mr. Thomas let out an experimental yell, but nobody answered. The noise could not even have reached his enemies.

4

Mike had gone home to bed, but the rest stayed. The question of leadership no longer concerned the gang. With nails, chisels, screwdrivers, anything that was sharp and penetrating, they moved around the inner walls worrying at the mortar between the bricks. They started too high, and it was Blackie who hit on the damp course and realized the work could be halved if they weakened the joints immediately above. It was a long, tiring, unamusing job, but at last it was finished. The gutted house stood there balanced on a few inches of mortar between the damp course and the bricks.

There remained the most dangerous task of all, out in the open at the edge of the bomb-site. Summers was sent to watch the road for passers-by, and Mr. Thomas, sitting on the loo, heard clearly now the sound of sawing. It no longer came from his house, and that a little reassured him. He felt less concerned. Perhaps the other noises too had no significance.

A voice spoke to him through the hole. "Mr. Thomas."

"Let me out," Mr. Thomas said sternly.

"Here's a blanket," the voice said, and a long grey sausage was worked through the hole and fell in swathes over Mr. Thomas' head.

"There's nothing personal," the voice said. "We want you to be comfortable tonight."

"Tonight," Mr. Thomas repeated incredulously.

"Catch," the voice said. "Penny buns—we've buttered them, and sausage-rolls. We don't want you to starve, Mr. Thomas."

Mr. Thomas pleaded desperately. "A joke's a joke, boy. Let me out and I won't say a thing. I've got rheumatics. I got to sleep comfortable."

"You wouldn't be comfortable, not in your house, you wouldn't. Not now."

"What do you mean, boy?" But the footsteps receded. There was only the silence of night: no sound of sawing. Mr. Thomas tried one more yell, but he was daunted and rebuked by the silence—a long way off an owl hooted and made away again on its muffled flight through the soundless world.

At seven next morning the driver came to fetch his lorry. He climbed into the seat and tried to start the engine. He was vaguely aware of a voice shouting, but it didn't concern him. At last the engine responded and he backed the lorry until it touched the great wooden shore that supported Mr. Thomas' house. That way he could drive right out and down

55

the street without reversing. The lorry moved forward, was momentarily checked as though something were pulling it from behind, and then went on to the sound of a long rumbling crash. The driver was astonished to see bricks bouncing ahead of him, while stones hit the roof of his cab. He put on his brakes. When he climbed out the whole landscape had suddenly altered. There was no house beside the car-park, only a hill of rubble. He went round and examined the back of his lorry for damage, and found a rope tied there that was still twisted at the other end round part of a wooden strut.

The driver again became aware of somebody shouting. It came from the wooden erection which was the nearest thing to a house in that desolation of broken brick. The driver climbed the smashed wall and unlocked the door. Mr. Thomas came out of the loo. He was wearing a grey blanket to which flakes of pastry adhered. He gave a sobbing cry. "My house," he said. "Where's my house?"

"Search me," the driver said. His eye lit on the remains of a bath and what had once been a dresser and he began to laugh. There wasn't anything left anywhere.

"How dare you laugh," Mr. Thomas said. "It was my house. My house."

"I'm sorry," the driver said, making heroic efforts, but when he remembered the sudden check to his lorry, the crash of bricks falling, he became convulsed again. One moment the house had stood there with such dignity between the bomb-sites like a man in a top hat, and then, bang, crash, there wasn't anything left—not anything. He said, "I'm sorry. I can't help it, Mr. Thomas. There's nothing personal, but you got to admit it's funny."

THE WATCH

Ivan Turgenev

1

I shall tell you my story about the watch.

A curious story!

It happened at the very beginning of this century, in 1801. I was just on sixteen. I was living in Ryazan, in a small frame house not far from the banks of the Oka, with my father, my aunt, and my cousin. I don't remember my mother; she died three years after her marriage; my father had no children but me. His name was Porphiry Petrovich. He was a tame man, plain-faced and rather sickly; he acted as an agent in legal—and other—business. In the old days people like him were called "scriveners," "pettifoggers," "nettleseed." He styled himself a "private attorney." His sister, my aunt, kept house for us—an old maid of fifty. (My father was over forty too.) She was a very pious woman—to put it bluntly, a hypocritical bigot; and a tell-tale—she poked her nose into everything; and, unlike my father, she was not kindhearted. We were— not poor, but we had only just enough. My father also had a brother, Igor by name, but because of certain alleged "subversive acts and a Jacobinical way of thinking" (that was the wording of the edict) he had been sent to Siberia as far back as 1797.

Igor's son David, my cousin, was left on my father's hands and lived with us. He was only one year older than I, but I worshipped him and did what he said as if he were quite grown-up. He was a bright boy, a boy of character; in build he was broad-shouldered and thickset; his face was square and covered with freckles; his hair was red; his eyes were gray and small; his lips were full; his nose, short; his fingers, short too—he was what is known as a "fine sturdy boy"—and strong beyond his years! My aunt could not endure him, and my father actually went in fear of him . . . or it may be he felt guilty towards him. It was rumored that if my father had not talked loosely and given his brother away—they would not have exiled David's father to Siberia! We were both studying at the high school, in the same class, and were both doing fairly well; as a matter of fact I was somewhat better than David—I had a good memory; but as everybody knows boys do not value *that* kind of superiority or take pride in it, and David remained nonetheless my leader.

2

I'm called Alexey, you know. I was born on the 7th, and my "name-day" is the 17th of March. In accordance with the ancient custom they gave me the name of one of the saints whose feast falls on the tenth day after the day of birth. My godfather was a certain Anastasy Anastasyevich Puchkov—or, really, Nastasey Nastaseich; no one called him anything but that. He was a frightful trouble-maker, a shyster, and bribe-taker—a bad man altogether. They had expelled him from the Governor's Chancery, and he was prosecuted more than once; but my father found him necessary. . . . They were "in business" together. In shape he was pudgy, quite round; but his face was like a fox's with a nose like an awl; his eyes were brown and beady, also like a fox's. And he would dart those eyes about, right and left, and point with his nose too, as if he were sniffing the air. He wore shoes without heels to them and powdered his hair every day, which was considered most unusual at that time, in the provinces. He told people that he could not go about unpowdered as he had to associate with generals and generals' ladies.

Well, so my name-day arrived! Nastasey Nastaseich came to our house and said:

"Up till now I have never given you anything, godson; but, to make up for it, just look at the kickshaw I've brought you today!"

And then he took from his pocket a silver watch—onion-shaped, with a rose painted on the face, and a brass chain. I was beside myself with joy; but my aunt, Pucheria Petrovna, practically yelled at me:

"Kiss his hand, kiss his hand, brat!"

I began to kiss my godfather's hand, but my aunt went right on lamenting:

"Ah, dear Nastasey Nastaseich, why do you spoil him so? How can he ever take care of a watch? He's sure to drop it, he'll break it, or take it to pieces!"

My father came in, looked at the watch, thanked Nastasey—rather perfunctorily; and then asked him into his study. And I heard my father say, as to himself:

"If you think you're going to get out of it *that* way, brother!"

But I couldn't stand still any longer. I put the watch on and dashed off headlong to show my present to David.

3

David took the watch, opened it, and examined it carefully. He had a strong mechanical bent; he loved to tinker with iron, copper, all kinds of metals; he had provided himself with various tools, and he thought nothing of repairing screws, keys, and so on, or even making new ones.

David turned the watch around in his hands and, after muttering through his teeth (he was never a great talker): "Old . . . not much good . . ." he added:

"Where from?"

I told him that my godfather had given it to me.

David turned his gray eyes on me.

"Nastasey?"

"Yes; Nastasey Nastaseich."

David laid the watch on the table and moved away without saying anything.

"Don't you like it?" I asked.

"No; it isn't that . . . but if I were you I wouldn't have accepted any present from Nastasey."

"Why?"

"Because he's filthy trash, and it isn't right to be under obligations to trash . . . And then say thank you to him on top of it . . . I bet you kissed his hand?"

"Yes, Aunt made me."

David smiled—in a special way, distending his nostrils. Such was his habit. He never laughed out loud; he considered laughter a sign of petty-mindedness.

David's words, his silent little smile, hurt me deeply. So, I thought, inwardly he disapproves of *me*. So *I'm* trash in his eyes, too. *He* would never have stooped to that, would not have accepted a present from Nastasey. But what am I to do now?

Give the watch back? Impossible!

I tried to discuss it with David, ask his advice. He replied that he never gave anyone advice and that I must act as I thought best. As I thought best! I remember that afterwards I didn't sleep all night. I was in a torment of indecision. I hated to part with the watch. I had put it beside my bed, on the little night table; it was ticking away so nicely, so entertainingly . . . But to feel that David despised me (Yes, let's face it! he despises me!) . . . that seemed to me unbearable. Towards morning, a resolution developed and ripened within me. I shed a few tears, it's true, but on the other hand I did go to sleep, and as soon as I woke up I dressed quickly and ran out into the street. I had made up my mind to give my watch away to the first poor person I should meet.

4

I had not run far from the house when I met with just what I was looking for. I came upon a ten-year-old boy, a barefoot ragamuffin who often sauntered past our windows. I raced up to him then and there and, without giving either him or me time to collect our wits, I offered him my watch.

The boy goggled at me; he shielded his mouth with one hand, as if he were afraid of getting burnt—and held out the other.

"Take it, take it," I mumbled. "It's mine, I'm giving it to you—you can sell it and buy yourself . . . Well, something you need . . . Goodbye!"

I thrust the watch into his hand and went home at top speed. After a brief pause outside the door of the bedroom we shared, to recover my breath, I approached David, who had just finished dressing and was brushing his hair.

"Do you know what, David," I began, in as calm a voice as I could, "I've given that watch of Nastasey's away."

David looked at me and drew the brush down over the front of his hair.

"Yes," I said in the same matter-of-fact tone, "I've given it away. There's this boy out there, very poor, he hasn't a thing; well, I gave it to him."

David put the hairbrush down on the wash-stand.

"With the money he makes on it," I went on, "he can get something useful. He'll get *something* for it, all the same."

I paused.

"Well! A good job!" David pronounced at last, and went off to class.

I followed him.

"And if they ask you what you've done with it?" He turned back to me.

"I'll say I lost it," I answered carelessly.

The two of us had no more talk about the watch that day, but all the same I had the feeling that David not only approved of me but . . . to a certain extent . . . even admired me. Honestly!

5

Two more days went by. As it turned out, nobody at our house missed the watch. My father was having a serious unpleasantness with one of his clients; he had no time for me or my watch. I, on the other hand, thought of it unceasingly. Even the approval—the presumed approval—of David did not console me too much. Indeed, he did not show it in any particular way: only said once—and that just in passing—that he had not expected such nerve of me.

Decidedly, my sacrifice had left me the loser; it was not counterbalanced by the gratification which my vanity supplied.

And then on top of it, as if by design, another boy we knew at the high school, the son of the town doctor, turned up and began to boast about a new watch that his grandmother had given him—and not silver, but pinchbeck.

At last I could take it no longer; and slipping furtively out of the house I went and hunted for the beggar boy to whom I had given my watch.

I soon found him. He was playing knucklebones on the church porch with some other boys. I called him aside and, choking, getting tangled up in my speech, I told him that my family were angry with me for giving the watch away and that if he would consent to return it to me I would be glad to pay him for it. I had brought with me, to be on the safe side, an old Elizabeth rouble—my entire ready capital.

"Well I haven't got it, that watch of yours," the boy replied in a cross, whimpering voice. "My dad saw it on me and he took it away, and he was all set to whip me, too; 'You must have stolen it somewhere,' he says, 'what fool is going to *give* you a watch?' "

"And who is your father?"

"My father? Trophimich."

"But what is he? What is his job?"

"He's a veteran—a sarngint. And he hasn't any job. He mends old shoes, he stitches soles on. That's all the work he has. He lives off that."

"Where do you live? Take me to him."

"I'll take you, all right! You tell him, tell my dad, you did give me that watch. He's after me all the time. 'A thief, you're a thief!' and my mother's at it too: 'Who do you take after,' she says, 'turning out a thief?' "

I went off with the boy to his living quarters. They were in a hut which had no chimney to its fireplace, in the back yard of a factory which had burned down long, long ago and not been rebuilt. We found both Trophimich and his wife at home. The veteran "sarngint" was a tall old man, muscular and upright, with yellowish-gray whiskers, and unshaven chin, and a whole network of wrinkles on his cheeks and forehead. His wife looked older than he; her little red eyes winked despondently, shrunken into the depths of her unwholesomely puffy face. They both had some dark rags draped on them in place of clothes.

I explained to Trophimich what the matter was and why I had come. He heard me out in silence, not blinking once and not removing me from his blunt, strained, simple-soldier gaze.

"Baby tricks!" he said at last in a hoarse toothless bass. "Is *that* how noble gentlemen behave? If as Petka really didn't steal the watch, I'll give him one just for that—Whack! Don't play around with your betters! But if he *had* stolen it, that's not how I'd give it him, but whack! whack! whack! with the flat of a sabre, like the cavalry guard. Simple as that. What's it all mean? Eh? At 'em with the pikes! Here's a how-d'ye-do! Pah!"

This last exclamation, Trophimich uttered in falsetto. He was obviously in a quandary.

"If you are willing to return the watch to me, sir," I explained to him—I did not dare not say "sir," even though he was a common soldier—"then I'll be glad to pay you for it . . . Here's this rouble . . . I don't suppose it's worth more than that."

"We-ell!" Trophimich growled, no less at a loss, and, out of old habit, devouring me with his eyes as if I were some commanding officer. "What a business—eh? Well, well, try to crack the nut—Shut up, Juliana!" he snapped at his wife, who was opening her mouth. "Here's the watch," he added, opening a table drawer. "If it's really yours, then kindly take it; but what is that rouble for? Hey?"

"Take the rouble, Trophimich, you useless creature!" howled his wife. "You've gone out of your mind in your old age. Not three kopecks to our name and there he is, putting on airs! They wasted their time when they cut your hair, you're still just an old woman! How can you be so stupid! *Take* the money, if you've really got it in your head to give the watch back!"

"Juliana, shut up, you slut!" repeated Trophimich. "Who ever saw the likes of it, all this jaw? Eh? The husband is the head, and is *she* to go jawing away? Petka, don't you move or I'll kill you! . . . There's the watch!"

Trophimich held the watch out to me, but he did not let go of it.

He thought, looked down; then he gave me that intent obtuse stare again and barked out abruptly at the top of his voice:

"Well where is it? Where's the rouble?"

"Here it is, here," I said hastily and pulled the coin out of my pocket.

But he did not take it, but kept staring at me. I laid the rouble on the table. Suddenly he swept it into the drawer, flung me the watch, and, making a sharp left turn and stamping his foot down hard, hissed at his wife and son:

"Get out, you scum!"

Juliana began to babble something—but I had already darted out into the yard, into the street. Thrusting the watch to the very bottom of my pocket, and gripping it tight, I went tearing home.

6

I had taken possession of the watch again, but it gave me no satisfaction. I could not bring myself to wear it: above all it was necessary to hide what I had done from David. What would he think of me, of my lack of character? I couldn't even shut that disastrous watch up in a drawer: we shared all our drawers in common. I had to hide it sometimes on top of the wardrobe, sometimes under the mattress, sometimes behind the stove—and for all that I did not succeed in fooling David!

One day, when I had taken the watch out from under a floorboard of our bedroom, it came into my head to rub its silver back with an old chamois-leather glove. David was off in town somewhere; I didn't in the least expect him back soon, but all of a sudden—there he was in the door!

I was so confused that I nearly dropped the watch, and, all flustered, my face turning so red that it hurt, I began to fumble along my waistcoat with the watch, quite unable to find the pocket.

David looked at me and, as usual, smiled quietly.

"What's the matter with you?" he asked at last. "You think I didn't know you have the watch again? The very first day you brought it back I saw it."

"I assure you—" I began, on the verge of tears.

David shrugged.

"It's your watch; you're free to do as you like with it."

Having said these hard words he went out.

Despair came over me. This time, there was no doubt about it: David really did despise me.

Things could not be left like this.

"I'll show him," I thought, clenching my teeth; and instantly, with a resolute step, I proceeded to the front hall, found our page boy Yushka, and presented the watch to him!

Yushka was going to refuse it, but I declared that if he did not take the watch from me I would bash it that very minute, stamp on it, smash it into smithereens, and throw it into the cesspool. He thought a moment, teehee'd, and took the watch. And I went back to our room and, seeing David there reading a book, told him of my deed. . . .

David did not take his eyes from the page and again, shrugging his shoulders and smiling to himself, said the watch was mine, and it was up to me. . . .

But it seemed to me that already he was a little less contemptuous of me.

I was quite convinced that I should nevermore expose myself to a fresh reproach for spinelessness; for that watch, the odious gift of my odious godfather, had suddenly become so loathsome to me that I was simply unable to understand how I could have regretted its loss, how I could have wheedled it back from someone like Trophimich: who still had a right, furthermore, to feel that he had treated me magnanimously!

Several days passed . . . I remember, on one of them a great piece of news finally made its way to our town: the Emperor Paul was dead and his son Alexander, of whose graciousness and humanity there were such good reports, had ascended the throne. This news excited David terribly: he at once envisaged the possibility of a reunion—a speedy reunion—with his father. My father rejoiced too.

"Now they'll be bringing all the exiles back from Siberia, and I daresay they won't forget brother Igor!" he kept repeating, rubbing his hands together gently, coughing, and at the same time seeming a little frightened.

David and I at once left off working and going to school; we did not even go out for walks, but just sat in a corner and calculated, and speculated, how many months, how many weeks, how many days it would take for "brother Igor" to come home, and where we should write to him, and how we could go to meet him, and how we should set about living afterwards. "Brother Igor" was an architect; David and I decided that the thing would be for him to move to Moscow and there build great schools for poor people, and we would go along as his assistants.

Of course we completely forgot about the watch; for that matter David was preoccupied by new anxieties . . . of them I'll speak later; but the watch was fated to remind us of its existence again.

7

One morning we had just finished breakfast—I was sitting alone at the window thinking about my uncle's return; an April thaw steamed and sparkled outside—when Pulcheria Petrovna came rushing into the room. At any time she was very quick and jumpy, and would speak in a high squeaky voice and gesticulate; and now she simply flew at me.

"Go! Go on! to your father at once, sir!" she shrilled. "Fine games you've been up to, shameless boy that you are! Now you're in for it, both of you! Nastasey Nastaseich has brought all your tricks to light. Go on! Your father's calling you. Go this instant!"

Still not understanding a thing, I followed my aunt—and, once I had crossed the drawing-room threshold, saw my father striding back and forth running his fingers through his hair, Yushka in tears by the door, and in the corner, on a chair, my godfather Nastasey Nastaseich—an expression of a peculiar sort of malignant joy in his dilated nostrils and his glinting, squinting little eyes.

No sooner had I entered than my father swooped down on me:

"Did *you* give the watch to Yushka? Answer!"

I glanced at Yushka.

"Answer me!" my father repeated, stamping his foot.

"Yes," I replied, and promptly received a hard slap in the face, which gave great pleasure to my aunt: I heard her yelp as if she had swallowed a mouthful of scalding tea. My father bounded from me to Yushka:

"And you, you scoundrel, you had no business daring to accept the watch as a gift," he added, yanking him about by the hair; "and on top of that you went and sold it, you good-for-nothing!"

As I learned later, Yushka actually had, in the simplicity of his heart, taken my watch to the neighboring clockmaker; the clockmaker put it in his window-front; Nastasey Nastaseich, passing by, saw it, bought it back, and brought it to our house.

However, our trial and punishment did not last long; my father got out of breath and went into a paroxysm of coughing; and anyway it wasn't in character for him to keep up a state of anger.

"Brother, Porphiry Petrovich," said my aunt as soon as she observed (not, to be sure, without some regret) that my father's rage had so to speak gone flying off; "please don't upset yourself any longer; it isn't worth dirtying your hands. But here is what I suggest: with the consent of our respected friend Nastasey Nastaseich, and since your son here is so basely ungrateful, *I* shall take charge of the watch myself; and since he has shown by his conduct that he is unworthy to have it, and doesn't even appreciate its value, I shall give it in your name to a person who will really feel your kindness."

"Who's that?" asked my father.

"Why, Chrisanth Lukich," replied my aunt, faltering slightly.

"Chrissy?" my father asked again; and, waving his hand, he added: "All one to me. Throw it in the stove for all I care."

He buttoned up his jacket, which had come undone, and went out, convulsed by a cough.

"And you, my dear sir, are you agreeable?" My aunt turned to Nastasey Nastaseich.

"Perfectly agreeable," he replied.

For the whole duration of our "trial and punishment" he had not moved in his chair, but only, quietly snuffling and rubbing his fingertips quietly together, turned his fox eyes in turn on me, on my father, on Yushka. We'd give him real satisfaction!

My aunt's proposal outraged me to the bottom of my soul. I didn't care about the watch, but I absolutely hated the man she meant to give it to. This Chrisanth Lukich, whose surname was Trankvillitatin, a husky, hefty, leggy student at the theological seminary, had fallen into the habit of coming to our house, the devil knows why. "To help the *children* with their studies," my aunt told people; but help us he could not, for the simple reason that he himself had never learned anything, and was as stupid as a horse. He was like a horse altogether: he clomped his feet like hooves; he did not laugh, but neighed, showed the whole inside of his mouth, too, right down to the windpipe; and he had a long face, a hump nose, and great flat jawbones; he wore a hairy frieze tunic belted at the waist, and smelled of raw meat. My aunt doted on him and called him a fine figure of a man, a cavalier, nay, a grenadier! He had a habit of tapping children on the forehead with the nails of his long fingers, hard as stones (he did it to me too, when I was younger), and as he tapped he would go "Haw! Haw!" and profess surprise: "I say, how that head of yours echoes! It must be empty." And this lout was to have my watch! "Not for anything!" I decided in my own mind, running out of the drawing room and getting up on my bed feet and all, while my cheek flamed from the slap I had received and my heart flamed, too, from the bitterness of the insult and a craving for revenge—not for anything! I would not let that damned theologue dishonor me. . . . He'd put on the watch, drape the chain over his stomach, whinny with delight . . . Not for anything!

All very well; but how could it be helped? How was I to prevent it?

I decided to steal the watch from my aunt!

8

Luckily Trankvillitatin was somewhere out of town at the time; he could not come to our house before tomorrow; I would have to take advantage of this night. My aunt did not lock herself into her bedroom; indeed in our house none of the keys worked in the locks; but where would she put the watch, where would she hide it? Till evening, she carried it in her pocket and more than once she even took it out and looked at it: but at night—where would it be at night? Well, it was my job to find out, I thought, shaking my fists.

I was all ablaze with daring, and horror, and joy, at the approach of the crime I so longed for—I kept nodding my head; I knit my brows; I whispered: "Just you wait!" I threatened somebody, I was villainous, I was dangerous . . . and I avoided David! Nobody, not even he, must have the slightest suspicion of what I meant to do.

I would carry it out alone—and alone I would take the responsibility!

Slowly the day trailed on . . . then the evening . . . at last night fell. I did nothing; I even tried not to move; one thought was driven fast in my head, like a nail. After lunch my father, whose anger, as I have said, was easily appeased . . . and besides he was rather ashamed of his violence: you do not slap sixteen-year-old boys in the face—my father tried to fondle me, but I rebuffed his advances, not out of rancor, as he imagined then, but it was simply that I was afraid of my feelings being shredded; I needed to preserve in their integrity all the fiery heat of my vengefulness, all the tempered hardness of my unalterable resolution! I went to bed very early but of course did not go to sleep and did not even close my eyes, but on the contrary kept them wide open, though I pulled the blanket over my head.

I had not considered ahead of time how to act; I had no plan whatsoever; I was merely waiting till at last everything in the house should quiet down. I had taken just one measure: I had not removed my stockings. My aunt's room was on the upper floor. I must go through the dining room and the front hall, go up the stairs, go along a little corridor—and then, the door on the right! No need to take a candle or a lantern with me: in a corner of my aunt's room, in front of the icon case, burned a little lamp that never went out; that I knew. So I would be able to see. I continued to lie there with my eyes staring wide and my mouth open and dry; the blood pounded in my temples, my ears, my throat, my back, my entire body. I waited . . . but it was as if some demon were making game of me. . . . The time went by . . . went by, but silence did not settle down!

Never, it seemed to me, had David taken so long to drop off to sleep. . . . David, taciturn David, actually chatted with me! Never had they banged about so in the house, and moved about so here and there, and talked. "And what are they talking *about*?" I wondered. "Haven't they been jabbering since morning?" Outside noises did not stop for a long time either; a dog barked a high persistent bark; a drunken peasant was rampaging somewhere and would not be controlled; gates kept creaking; a wagon came along on wobbly wheels, kept coming and coming and would not pass by! However, *these* sounds did not irritate me; on the contrary I was glad of them, somehow; they seemed to distract my attention. . . . But now at last everything seemed to have settled down. Only the pendulum of our old clock hoarsely and solemnly ticked in the dining room, and I could hear the even, long-drawn-out, labored-sounding breathing of people asleep. I was about to get up—but something rustled again . . . there was a sudden groan . . . something soft fell down . . . a whispering seemed to spread out and slither along the walls. . . .

Or was there no such thing, and was it only my imagination teasing me?

At last all was still. It was the very heart and dark and deep of the night—*now* is the time! Chilly all over beforehand, I throw off the bedclothes, lower my feet to the floor, stand up . . . one step; another . . . I steal along. My feet, as if they belonged to someone else, heavy, tread weakly and unsteadily. Stop! What's that sound? Someone, somewhere, is sawing, or scratching—or sighing? I listen . . . Prickles run over my cheeks, and watery, cold tears come into my eyes . . . Nothing! I slink on again. It's dark, but I know the way. Suddenly I stumble on a chair—what a bang, and how it hurts! It hit me just on the shin . . . I freeze in my tracks. Will they wake up? Ah! Who cares! All at once daring and even fury make their appearance—Forward! Forward! There's the dining room crossed, there's the door groped for—opened at one go, with a flourish—the damned hinge squeaks, confound it! But I'm already going up the stairs—one, two! one, two! A step has creaked under my foot: I gave it a vicious look, as if I could see it. Now I'm pulling another door by the handle, gradually. Not a sound from this one! Lightly it swings itself wide open—"Do come in," it says, "you're welcome!" And here I am in the corridor.

High up in the corridor, just under the roof, there is a little window. The faint light of the night barely sifts in through the dark panes. And by that glimmering light I see our little errand girl lying on the floor, on a felt mat, both hands thrown up beside her tousled head; she is sound asleep, breathing rapidly; and just behind her head is the fateful door. I step over the mat, over the little girl. Who opened that door for me I do not know, but here I am in my aunt's room. There is the icon lamp in one corner, and the bed in another, and my aunt, in a nightcap and a nightgown, on the bed, her face towards me. She's asleep and not stirring; I can't even hear her breathing. The flame of the little lamp wavers quietly, disturbed by the influx of cold air; and all over the room, even on my aunt's still, waxy-yellow face, the shadows flicker.

And there's the watch! It's hanging behind the bedstead, on the wall, on a little embroidered cushion. What luck, imagine! There need be no delay. But what are those footsteps, soft and swift, behind my back? Ah, no! that's my heart beating! I take a step forward—God! Something round, biggish, pushes against me below my knee—once! and once again! I am ready to shriek, ready to faint with horror. A tiger cat, our household cat, is standing in front of me, arching his back and lifting up his tail: he jumps up onto the bed, heavily and softly, turns round and sits down, without purring, like a judge: sits and looks at me with his golden pupils. "Puss, puss!" I whisper, just audibly. I lean over my aunt, I've actually seized the watch—all at once she raises herself a little and opens her eyelids wide. God our savior! What will happen now? But her eyelids quiver and close and with a faint murmur her head falls back upon the pillow.

A minute, and I'm back in my own room again, in my own bed—and the watch is in my hands.

Lighter than thistledown I flew back! I'm a bold bravo, I'm a robber, I'm a hero, I'm choking with joy, I'm burning hot, I'm gleeful—I want to wake David up right now and tell him all—and, incredible as it may be, I fall asleep and sleep the sleep of the dead. I open my eyes at last . . . It's light in the room, the sun has already risen. Luckily no one is awake yet. I leap up as if scalded, rouse David, and report it all to him. He listens, grins. "Do you know what?" he says to me at the end. "We'll bury that foolish watch in the ground so it'll never be heard of again." I find his idea superlative. In a few moments we're both dressed and run to the orchard behind our house. And under an old apple tree, in a deep hole hurriedly dug in the loose spring earth with David's big knife, my godfather's hateful present is buried forever—thus avoiding the hands of the loathsome Trankvillitatin! We stamp the hole smooth, scatter rubble over it, and proud, happy, quite unobserved, go back to the house, lie down in our beds, and sleep for another hour or so—and what a light and blissful sleep!

You can imagine the hullabaloo there was that morning the moment my aunt woke up and found the watch was missing. To this day her piercing shriek rings in my ears. "Help! I've been robbed! I've been robbed!" she screeched, and roused the whole house. She was raging mad. But David and I only smiled to ourselves, and sweet our smiling was to us!

"Everybody must be whipped, one after the other," cried my aunt. "They took the watch right from under my head, right from under my pillow!" We were prepared for anything: we expected trouble—but, contrary to our expectations, we did not get into trouble at all. At first my father did bluster terribly: he even mentioned the police; but evidently he was bored to begin with by yesterday's reprisals, and all of a sudden, to my aunt's indescribable amazement, he fell not on us but on her. "You make me sick and tired with your watch, Pulcheria Petrovna!" he shouted. "I don't want to hear any more about it. It didn't disappear by magic, you say; but what's that to me? What if it *was* magic! It was stolen from you? Well good riddance to it. What will Nastasey Nastaseich say? Well, the hell with him, your Nastaseich! From him I get nothing but dirty tricks and unpleasantness. Don't you dare to bother me anymore! Do you hear?" My father slammed the door and went off into his study. At first David and I did not understand the hint contained in his last words, but later we learned that my father was extremely indignant, just then, with my godfather, who had overbid him for a profitable piece of business.

So my aunt was left looking a fool. She nearly burst with vexation, but there was nothing to be done about it. She had to confine herself to twisting her mouth at me whenever she passed me and repeating over and over in a harsh whisper:

"Thief, thief, convict, cheat!" My aunt's objurgations gave me genuine enjoyment. It was very enjoyable also, going by the garden enclosure, to let my eye slide with sham indifference over towards the spot beneath the apple tree where the watch reposed and, if David was on hand too, to exchange a significant grimace with him.

My aunt took it into her head to set Trankvillitatin on me, but I applied to David for help. He straightway announced to the stalwart student of divinity that he would rip up his belly with a knife if he did not leave me alone. Trankvillitatin got scared; grenadier and cavalier though he was according to my aunt, he was not notable for courage.

So five weeks went by. But you don't think that the story of the watch ended there? No, it did not; only in order to continue my story I must introduce a new character; and to introduce this new character I shall have to go back a little.

11

For a long time my father had been friendly, even intimate, with a retired government clerk, Latkin, a lame little wretch of a man with shy, bizarre ways, one of those beings for whom the saying was invented that "God himself has martyred them." Like my father and Nastasey he handled miscellaneous legal affairs and was likewise a "private attorney" and agent; but having neither a dignified presence nor the gift of eloquence, and with too little self-confidence, he could not bring himself to operate independently, and joined up with my father. His handwriting was "absolute filigree-work," he knew the law inside out, and he comprehended to a nicety all the flourishes of legal and bureaucratic jargon. Together with my father he administered various affairs and shared the profits

and losses, and it seemed nothing could make their friendship totter: but for all that it crashed down to ruin in a single
day—and forever. My father fell out forever with his col-
league. If Latkin had nabbed some profitable commission
from him, after the style of Nastasey, who replaced him later,
my father would have been no more indignant with him
than he was with Nastasey—probably less, indeed. But
Latkin, under the influence of some obscure unaccountable
feeling—envy, greed, or perhaps even a momentary infusion
of honesty—let my father down, betrayed him to a common
client of theirs, a rich young merchant, opening the eyes of
this careless youth to a certain . . . a certain sharp practice
which was bound to bring considerable profit to my father.
It was not the financial loss, great as that might be, no! but
the treachery that offended my father and made him explode.
He could not forgive perfidiousness!

"Just see, we've a saint in our midst!" he repeated over and
over, trembling with rage, teeth chattering as if he had a fever.
I happened to be there, in the room, and was a witness of that
ugly scene. "Good! From this day forth—amen! It's all over
between us. There's the door. I'll never set foot in your house
again, or you in mine. You're too damned honest for us—how
can you and I be associates? But from now on may you have
neither house nor home!"

In vain did Latkin implore my father, bow to the ground
before him; in vain did he try to explain what filled his own
soul with painful bewilderment. "Look, I've made nothing by
it, have I, Porphiry Petrovich?" he stammered. "Look, it's my
own throat I've cut." My father remained inflexible. Latkin
had never again set foot in our house. Fate itself, it seemed,
intended to realize my father's last cruel wish. Soon after the
rupture (it took place two years before the beginning of my
story), Latkin's wife—who had already been ill for a long

time, it's true—died; his younger daughter, a three-year-old child, became deaf and dumb in one day, from shock; a swarm of bees had settled on her head. Latkin himself had an apoplectic stroke and sank into extreme, conclusive poverty. How he made ends meet, what he existed on, it was difficult to imagine. He lived in a tumble-down hovel at no great distance from our house. His elder daughter Raisa lived with him too and took care of the house—as far as that was possible. This Raisa is in fact the new character whom I have to bring into the story.

12

When her father was friends with mine, we used to see her all the time; sometimes she would spend an entire day with us, either sewing or spinning with her slender, nimble, and skillful hands. She was a graceful rather spare girl with intelligent brown eyes in a pale oval face. She talked little, but sensibly, in a low resonant voice, hardly opening her mouth and not showing her teeth; when she laughed—which seldom happened and never lasted long—she'd suddenly expose them all: big and white as almonds. I remember her walk, too: light, resilient, with a little lilt in every step; it always seemed to me she was going down a flight of stairs, even when she was walking on level ground. She held herself erect, with her arms folded tight across her breast. And whatever she did, whatever she undertook—were it only threading a needle, say, or pressing a skirt with a flat-iron—everything she did was beautiful and somehow . . . you won't believe it . . . touching. Her Christian name was Raisa, but we used to call her Chernogubkoy, "Black lip"; she had a tiny dark-blue birthmark on her upper lip, as if she'd been eating blackberries; but this did not mar her appearance; just the contrary. She was exactly one year older than David. I cherished for her a feeling rather like respect; but she had little to do with me. On the other hand, a friendship had grown up between her and David—an unchildlike, odd, but good friendship. They somehow *went* together. Sometimes they would not exchange a word for hours on end, but each of them felt that they were both happy—and happy precisely because they were together. I have not met another such girl, truly. There was something intent and resolute about her, something honest and sad and sweet. I never heard her say anything remarkably intelligent, but I never heard her say anything petty, either, and I have never seen more intelligent eyes. After the break occurred between her family and mine I did not see much of her; my father strictly forbade me to visit the Latkins, and she no longer appeared at our house. But I would meet her in the street and at church; and Black-lip always aroused the same feeling in me: respect and even a certain wonder, rather than pity. Indeed, she bore her tribulations very well. "A flint-maiden," the coarse-grained Trankvillitatin said of her one day. But actually pity *was* called for. Her face took on an anxious, weary expression; her eyes came to look pinched and sunken; a burden beyond her strength lay on her still childish shoulders.

David saw her far oftener than I; he even went to their house. My father did not make the gesture of forbidding it: he knew that David would not obey him anyway. And then from time to time Raisa would appear at the fence of our garden, which gave on a little side street, and see David there. It was not conversation that she came for; but she would tell him of some new difficulty or new misfortune—she would ask his advice. The paralysis that had struck Latkin was of a rather grotesque type. His arms and legs were weakened but he had not lost the use of them, and his brain, even, functioned properly; but his *speech* became confused and instead of certain words he would utter others; one had to guess at what he really wanted to say.

"Chu-chu-chu," he would stammer, with an effort—he began every phrase with "chu-chu-chu." "Scissors, give me some scissors." And scissors stood for bread. My father he hated with all the strength that was left to him; he attributed all his calamities to my father's curse and called him sometimes the butcher, sometimes the diamond-merchant. "Chu-chu, don't you dare go to the butcher's, Vassilyevna!" He had rechristened his daughter by this name: but his name was Martinyan, so that she was properly "Martinyanovna."* With each day he became more demanding; his needs increased . . . And how could those needs be satisfied? Where was the money to come from? Grief ages people early, but it was terrible to hear certain words on the lips of a girl of seventeen.

13

I remember it so happened that I was present at her conversation with David, at the fence, on the very day of her mother's death.

"Mummy died at dawn today," she said, looking around, first, with her dark expressive eyes and then fixing them on the ground; "The cook has undertaken to buy a coffin that doesn't cost much, but we can't rely on her, she may even spend the money on drink. If you'd come and look after it, Davey? She's afraid of you."

***Martinyanovna.** Daughter of Martinyan.

"I'll come," David answered. "I'll look after it. But how is your father?"

"He's crying; he's saying 'Bury me with her too!'—now he's fallen asleep." Raisa suddenly heaved a deep sigh. "Oh, Davey, Davey!" She passed her half-clenched little fist over her forehead and eyebrows; and this gesture was so poignant . . . and so unaffected, and so beautiful, like all her gestures!

"You must take care of yourself, though," observed David. "You've had no sleep at all, I suppose. . . . And what's the good of crying? It's no help in grief."

"I have no time for crying," Raisa answered.

"Rich people can indulge themselves that way, and cry," said David.

Raisa started to go, but turned back.

"They're bargaining for our yellow shawl—you know, from Mummy's dowry. They'll give twelve roubles. I don't think that's much."

"No, not much at all."

"We wouldn't sell it," Raisa said after a pause. "But you see we have to, for the funeral."

"Yes, you have to. Only it isn't right to give out money for nothing. Those priests are a curse! Well, then, just wait, and I'll come. Are you going? I'll be there soon. Goodbye, little pigeon."

"Goodbye, Davey, my dear!"

"Now mind you, don't cry!"

"What, cry? It's either cooking the dinner or crying. One of the two."

"How's that, cooking the dinner?" I turned to David as soon as Raisa had gone. "Is she really doing the cooking herself?"

"Well, you heard her, didn't you? The cook has gone to bargain for a coffin."

"She's cooking the dinner," I thought, "and her hands are

always so clean and her clothes are so tidy . . . I wish I could see what she's like there in the kitchen . . . An extraordinary girl!"

I remember another "fence conversation." This time Raisa brought her little deaf-and-dumb sister with her. She was a pretty child with huge wondering eyes and a whole mass of dull black hair on her little head. (Raisa's hair was black too—and hers too was without luster.) Latkin had been stricken by paralysis by now.

"I simply don't know what to do," began Raisa. "The doctor has written a prescription, I must go to the apothecary; and now here's our peasant" (the Latkins still had one serf) "has brought us some wood and a goose, from the village. But the landlord's man is taking it away from us. 'You're in arrears with me,' he says."

"He's taking the goose?" David asked.

"No, not the goose; it's old, he says, it's no good any longer, he says, that's why the peasant brought it to you. But he's taking the logs."

"But he has no right!" cried David.

"He has no right, but he's taking them. . . . I went up to the loft, there's a chest of ours standing there, old as anything. I began rummaging about in it and what should I find: look!"

She took from under her kerchief a good-sized telescope, brass-mounted and covered in yellowed morocco leather. David, as a lover and connoisseur of instruments of every kind, seized upon it instantly.

"English," he said, putting it first to one eye, then to the other. "Nautical!"

"And the lenses are perfect," Raisa went on. "I showed it to Father; he said 'Take it and pawn it to the diamond merchant!' Now what do you think? Will they give us cash for it! What should *we* do with a telescope? Look at ourselves in a mirror through it to see what beauties we are? But we have no mirror; what a pity!"

Having spoken these words Raisa suddenly began to laugh out loud.

Her little sister, of course, could not hear her, but probably she felt the shaking of her body; she was holding Raisa's hand—and raising her big eyes to her, her little face contorted with fright, she burst into tears.

"That's how she always is," observed Raisa. "She doesn't like it when people laugh."

"I won't, Lyubochka, I won't," she said, quickly dropping to sit on her heels beside the child, and running her fingers through her hair. "See?"

The laughter had vanished from Raisa's face, and her lips which had crooked up at the ends in a particularly endearing way, became motionless again. The child was quieted. Raisa got up.

"So Davey, you'll do what you can—with the telescope? Or it'll be too bad about the logs—and the goose too, however old it may be."

"They'll certainly give you ten roubles," said David, aiming the telescope in all directions. "*I'll* buy it from you—what could be better? Meanwhile, here's fifteen kopecks for the apothecary. . . . Is that enough?"

"I'll *borrow* this from you," whispered Raisa, taking the fifteen kopecks from him.

"Oh, of course. At interest—is that what you want? Why look, I have security for it here. A very valuable article! they're a first-rate country, the English."

"But they say we're going to war with them?"

"No," answered David. "We're fighting the French now."

"Well—you know best. So, do what you can, then. Goodbye, sirs!"

And here is yet another conversation that took place at that fence. Raisa seemed more than usually anxious.

"Five kopecks for a head of cabbage, and a wee little one at that," she said, propping her chin on her hand. "Prices are sky high! And the money for my sewing not in yet."

"Who owes it to you?" asked David.

"Why, the merchant's wife who lives on the other side of the rampart."

"The one who goes about in a green jacket—who's so fat?"

"That's the one."

"My word, she's fat! She can't breathe for fat, she practically gives off steam in church, but she doesn't pay her debts."

"She will pay . . . only, when? And besides, Davey, I have new worries. My father's taken it into his head to tell me his dreams. Well, you know he's become—cross-tongued; he wants to say one word and another comes out. When it's a question of food, or anything everyday, we've got used to it by now, we understand; but a dream isn't usually understandable even with well people; and *his* are—ghastly! 'I'm very happy,' he says. 'Today I was walking about all among the white birds; and the Lord God gave me a pooket, and inside the pooket was Andryushka with a little knife.'—He calls Lyubochka 'Andryushka.'—'Now,' he says, 'we shall both be quite well. All that's needed is one strrrike! with the little knife! Like this!' and he points to his throat. I don't understand him. I say 'All right, darling, all right,' but he gets angry; he wants to explain to me what it's all about. He even began to cry."

"Well, you could have told him something or other," I put in. "You could have made up some lie."

"I don't know how to lie," Raisa replied, and spread her hands hopelessly.

And, in fact, she did *not* know how to lie.

"No need to lie," said David, "but it doesn't follow you should kill yourself over it, either. You don't think anyone will thank you for it?"

Raisa looked at him intently.

"What I wanted to ask you, Davey: how do you write 'principal'?"

" 'Principal' used how?"

"Well, for instance: 'The principal thing is that you should live.' "

"Write it: p,r,i,n,c,i,p,l,e."

"No," I cut in, "not p,l,e, but p,a,l."

"Well, it's all the same, write: p,a,l! But the principal thing is that *you* should live!"

"I'd like to write correctly," Raisa observed, and blushed a little.

When she blushed she at once became wonderfully prettier.

"It may come in useful. How Daddy could write in his day! It was a marvel! And he gave me lessons. Well, now he is even bad at making out the letters."

"I'd just have you *live*—" said David, lowering his voice and not taking his eyes from her. Raisa threw a quick glance at him and turned still redder. "You live . . . and as for writing, write as best you can. . . . Oh, damn, the witch is coming!" (David called my aunt the witch.) "And what brings *her* here? Run along, my dear!"

Raisa glanced at David again and ran away.

David talked of Raisa and her family with me very rarely and reluctantly, especially from the time when he began to look for his father's return. He thought of nothing but that—and of how we should live afterwards. He remembered him vividly and described him to me with particular relish:

"Big, strong, he can lift three hundredweight with one hand! The way he would shout 'Hey, lad!'—you could hear him all over the house. He's so fine and kind . . . and is he brave! He was never afraid of anyone. We used to have a wonderful time, before we were ruined. They say he's gone completely gray now, but, before, his hair was as red as mine. He's a re-al cham-pion!"

David would not hear of our staying in Ryazan.

"You will go away," I said, "but I shall stay."

"Don't be silly, we'll take you with us."

"And what about my father?"

"You'll chuck your father. If you don't chuck him it will be the end of you."

"What do you mean?"

David did not answer me, only wrinkled his white forehead.

"So, when I go away with Father," he began again, "he'll find a good position, and I shall get married."

"Well, *that* won't be soon," I observed.

"No, and why not? I *shall* get married soon."

"You?"

"Yes, I; what of it?"

"I don't suppose you have your eye on your wife already?"

"Of course I have."

"Who is she then?"

David grinned.

"How thick-headed you are, though! Raisa, of course."

"Raisa!" I repeated in astonishment. "You're joking!"

"I wouldn't know how to joke, brother, *and* I don't like to."

"But isn't she a year older than you are?"

"What of it? But let's drop the subject."

"Let me ask one thing," I said. "Does she know that you intend to marry her?"

87

"Probably."

"But you haven't disclosed anything to her?"

"What is there to disclose? When the time comes I'll tell her. Now—that's enough of that."

David got up and went out of the room. Left alone, I thought . . . and I thought . . . and at last I decided that David was behaving like a sensible and practical man, and I felt flattered, indeed, at being the friend of such a practical man!

And Raisa, in her everlasting black wool dress, suddenly seemed to me charming and worthy of the most devoted love!

15

David's father still did not come and did not even send a letter. It had been summertime for ages; the month of June was drawing to an end. We were jaded with waiting. . . .

Meanwhile rumors began to circulate that Latkin had suddenly turned much worse and that his family would die of starvation any day now—if the house did not fall down and crush them all under the roof. David changed, even in looks, and became so bad-tempered and gloomy that you could hardly go near him. He began to be away from the house more often, too.

I had no encounters at all with Raisa. Now and then she would flit by at a distance, swiftly crossing the street, with her beautiful airy walk—straight as an arrow, arms folded—with her dark, intelligent gaze under her long eyebrows, and with a worried expression on her pale sweet face. And that was all.

My aunt, with the assistance of her Trankvillitatin, plagued me the same as before, and as before would whisper upbraidingly right into my ear: "You're a thief, sir, a thief!" But I paid no attention to her; and my father was busy, bustling about on errands here and there and working at his papers, and did not want to know a thing.

One day, passing by the familiar apple tree, I cast a sidelong glance, largely out of habit, at the well-known little spot, and it suddenly struck me that a change had taken place on the surface of the earth that covered our treasure. A sort of little hump showed where earlier there had been a hollow, and the bits of rubble weren't lying the same way as before! "What does this mean?" I wondered. "Can it be that someone has fathomed our secret and dug up the watch?"

I had to make sure with my own eyes. Of course I felt utterly indifferent to the watch so long as it rusted in the bowels of the earth: but I was not going to let anyone else enjoy the use of it! And so the very next day, rising at dawn again and arming myself with a knife, I went to the orchard, found the place in question under the apple tree, and pro-ceeded to dig; and when I had dug a hole more than two feet deep was forced to the conclusion that the watch had vanished, that someone had got at it, taken it out, stolen it.

But who could have . . . taken it out, except David?

Who else knew where it was?

I filled the hole in and went back to the house. I felt deeply injured.

"Supposing," I thought, "David needed the watch to save his future wife or her father from dying of hunger. . . . Say what you like, that watch is worth *something*. . . . Then why not come to me and say: 'Brother!' (in David's place I should most certainly have said "brother") 'Brother! I am in need of money; you have none, I know, but let me have the use of that watch that you and I buried together beneath the old apple tree! It's not doing anyone any good, and I shall be so grateful to you, brother!' How joyfully I should have consented! But to act underhandedly, treacherously, not to trust his friend! . . . No, no passion, no need can excuse that!"

I repeat, I was terribly offended. I began to treat David coldly, to sulk. . . .

But David was not a person to notice a thing like that and be upset.

I began dropping hints.

But David didn't seem to understand my hints in the slightest.

I said in front of him how low, in my eyes, was the man who, having a friend, and understanding the full meaning of the sacred sentiment of Friendship, was yet so lacking in magnanimity as to resort to deceit: as if it were possible to hide a thing!

Pronouncing these last words, I laughed contemptuously.

But David didn't turn a hair.

At last I asked him outright, what did he suppose, had our watch kept going for a while after being buried in the ground, or had it stopped immediately?

He answered me:

"The devil only knows! Is that the best you can find to think about?"

I did not know what to think. Obviously David had something on his mind . . . but not the theft of the watch. An unexpected event demonstrated his innocence to me.

16

One day I came home by way of a side street which I ordinarily avoided taking because the house where my enemy Trankvillitatin lodged was in it; but on this occasion fate itself led me there. Passing the open window of a tea house

I suddenly heard the voice of our servant Vassily, a cheeky young fellow, a great "lazybones and scallywag," my father called him—but also a great conqueror of women's hearts, on which he operated by means of quips, dancing, and strumming on a torban.

"And just wait till you hear what they concocted," said Vassily—whom I could not see, but heard quite distinctly: he was probably sitting right there by the window with a comrade, over their steaming tea, and, as often happens with people in a room with the door shut, was talking in a loud voice without suspecting that every passer-by in the street could hear every word. "What did they concoct? They buried it in the ground!"

"They never!" grumbled another voice.

"You have it from me! That's what extryordinary young gentlemen we have at our house. Especially that David . . . what an Aesop he is. I got up right at crack of dawn and I goes to the window . . . I look out: what in the world? Our two little pigeons are going along in the orchard, they're carrying that very watch, they dig a hole under an apple tree—and there they put it—just like it was a baby! And then they smooth up the ground, as true as I'm alive, the young wastrels."

"Ah, deuce take them," said Vassily's companion. "Comes of being spoiled, that's what. Well, and then what? Did you dig up the watch?"

"Naturally I dug it up. I have it right now. Only it won't do to show it for the time being. There was an awful noise on account of it. That Alexey'd pinched it that very night, right from under our old lady's backbone."

"O-oh!"

"You have it from me! He's bold as brass. So I can't show it. But the officers will be coming; I'll sell it to one of them, or else I'll stake it at cards."

I did not wait to hear more. I dashed home and straight to David.

"Brother!" I began. "Brother! Forgive me! I've done you wrong! I suspected you! I blamed you! You see how upset I am. Forgive me!"

"What's the matter with you?" asked David. "Explain!"

"I suspected you of digging up our watch from under the apple tree."

"That watch again! You mean it's not there?"

"It's not there; I thought you'd taken it to help your friends. And all the time it was Vassily!"

I reported to David everything I had heard under the tea house window.

But how can I describe my amazement! Of course I had expected David to be indignant; but I could not possibly have foreseen what did come over him—scarcely had I finished my story when he flew into an unspeakable fury! David who had never shown anything but contempt for the whole—in his words—"petty" escapade of the watch, that very David who had more than once declared that the watch wasn't worth a rotten egg—*he* suddenly jumped up from his seat, blazed scarlet, ground his teeth, clenched his fists. "We can't let this pass," he said at last. "How dare he appropriate some-one else's property! I'll show him; just wait! I will not connive at theft!"

I confess, to this day I do not understand what could have maddened David so; whether he was already irritated, quite apart from this, and Vassily's behavior only poured oil on the fire; whether my suspicions offended him, I cannot say: but I had never seen him in such a state. I stood before him open-mouthed and simply marveled at his breathing so heavy and hard.

"What do you intend to do?" I asked at last.

"You'll see, after lunch, when your father lies down. I'll find that joker. I'll have a little talk with him."

"Well," I thought, "I shouldn't like to be in that *joker's* place. What will happen now? Lord, my God!"

17

What did happen was this:

After lunch, as soon as that sleepy stuffy stillness settled down which to this day lies like a warm featherbed over a Russian house and Russian people in the middle of the day after they have fed, David (I followed at his heels with fainting heart)—David went to the servants' quarters and called Vassily out. He would not come at first, but ended by obeying and following us to the orchard.

"Vassily Terentyev!" my comrade began in a firm voice. "Six weeks ago you took from under this apple tree here a watch we'd hidden. You had no right to do it, it didn't belong to you. Give it back this minute!"

Vassily was almost disconcerted, but recovered himself immediately. "What watch? What are you talking about? Lord love you! I haven't any watch."

"I know what I'm talking about, and don't you lie. You have got the watch. Give it back!"

"I haven't got your watch."

"Then how was it that at the tea house you—" I began, but David stopped me.

"Vassily Terentyev!" he said in a hollow menacing voice. "We know for a fact that you have the watch. I'm giving you a fair chance to hand it back. But if you don't . . ."

Vassily fleered impudently. "And what will you do to me then, sir—hey?"

"What? We'll both fight you, till either you beat us or we beat you."

Vassily laughed. "Fight? That's no business for gentlemen! Fight with a serf?"

David suddenly grabbed Vassily by the waistcoat.

"But we won't be fighting you with our fists," he said, gnashing his teeth. "Do you understand! But I'll give you a knife, and I'll take one myself—then we'll see who wins— Alexey!" he commanded me. "Run and get my big knife, you know, it has a bone handle; it's lying there on the table; and I have another one in my pocket."

Vassily suddenly caved in. David still held him tight by the waistcoat. "For pity's sake—for pity's sake, David Igorich," he stammered; tears actually started to his eyes. "What's come over you? What's the matter with you? Let go of me!"

"I won't let go of you—and you'll get no quarter. If you get away from us today we'll begin all over again tomorrow. Alyosha! Where's that knife?"

"David Igorich!" howled Vassily. "Don't commit murder! What is all this? The watch—I—the fact is, I was playing a little joke. I'll give it back to you this very moment. How can you act like this? One moment you're going to rip up Chrisanth Lukich's belly—now me! Let me go, David Igorich, please accept the watch. Only don't tell the papa!"

David released his hold on Vassily's waistcoat. I looked at his face. Indeed it was enough to frighten others besides Vassily. So bleak . . . and cold . . . and vindictive.

Vassily bounded to the house and came right back with the watch in his hand. He gave it to David without saying anything, and only on returning to the house again did he exclaim in a loud voice, on the threshold: "Phew—what goings-on!"

He was still completely out of countenance. David shook his head and went to our room. Again I trailed after him. "A Suvarov! He's a real Suvarov!" I thought to myself. At that time, 1801, Suvarov was our great national hero.

18

David shut the door behind him, laid the watch on the table, folded his arms, and—oh, wonder! burst out laughing. Looking at him I laughed too.

"What an amazing box of tricks!" he began. "We simply cannot get rid of this watch! It's bewitched, honestly! And why did I fly off the handle like that?"

"Yes, why?" I repeated. "You might have let Vassily keep it."

"Oh, no," David interrupted. "That's ridiculous. But what shall we do with it now?"

"Yes, what?"

We both stared at the watch and pondered.

Adorned with a string of blue glass beads (in his haste poor Vassily hadn't managed to remove these beads, which belonged to him), it was placidly doing its work: it was ticking—rather spasmodically, it's true—and slowly moving its copper minute hand around.

"Bury it again, maybe? Or throw it into the stove?" I suggested at last. "Or look, why not present it to Latkin?"

"No," replied David, "that won't do at all. But here's what: at the Governor's Chancery they've set up a committee, they're collecting contributions in aid of the Kasimovians who have lost their things in the fire. They say the town of Kasimov is burned to a cinder—churches and all. And they

95

say they'll accept anything there—not just food and money but all kinds of things. Let's donate the watch to them! Eh?"

"Yes, let's!" I caught him up. "A fine idea! But I thought, since your friends are in need . . ."

"No, no, the committee! The Latkins can manage without *it*. Give it to the committee!"

"Well then, the committee be it. Only I suppose we have to write something about it, to the Governor."

David looked at me.

"You think so?"

"Yes; of course, there's no need to write much. But, you know, a few words."

"For instance?"

"For instance, begin like this: 'We, being' . . . Or, better still: 'Moved by compassion' . . ."

" 'Moved by compassion': good."

"Then we should say: 'we enclose herewith our mite.' "

" 'Mite' . . . that's good, too. Well, get a pen, sit down and write, go on!"

"A rough draft first," I said.

"All right, a rough draft, only write, write! . . . Meanwhile I'll clean it with some whiting."

I took a sheet of paper and cut a new point for a quill, but I hadn't had time to trace at the top of the sheet: "To his Excellency his Lordship the gracious Prince" (our Governor was then Prince X) when I stopped, struck by an extraordinary hubbub that had suddenly arisen in the house.

David had also noticed this noise and also stopped what he was doing, holding the watch up in his left hand and a little rag with whiting on it in his right. We looked at each other. What was that shrill cry? It was our aunt, screaming; and *that*? that was the voice of my father, hoarse with rage. "The watch! the watch!" somebody yelled—why, that was Trankvillitatin.

Feet clattered, floorboards creaked, there was a perfect mob running—and they were rushing straight towards us! I stood stock-still with fear, and even David went white as clay— but he looked dauntless as an eagle. "Vassily's betrayed us, the villain," he hissed between his teeth. The door flew open wide—and my father, in his dressing gown, without his cra- vat, my aunt in her powdering cape, Trankvillitatin, Vassily, Yushka, another boy, the cook Agapit—they all irrupted into the room.

"You vile young beasts!" cried my father, scarcely able to breathe—"At last we've caught you in the act!" And, seeing the watch in David's hand, "Give it here!" my father bel- lowed. "Give me the watch!"

But David, without speaking a word, sprang to the open window—and leaped out into the yard—into the street!

Accustomed to imitate my model in everything, I jumped out too; I ran after David.

"Catch them! Hold them!" wild voices roared after us in medley.

But we were already tearing down the street, bareheaded, David in the lead and I a few steps behind him; and at our back the trampling and din of the chase!

19

Many years have gone by since the time of all these events; I have reflected on them more than once; and to this day I cannot understand the reason for the rage that possessed my father, who had so recently forbidden the very mention of the watch in his presence, it bored him so—just as I could not understand then David's frenzy at the news that Vassily had stolen it. In spite of myself I toy with the idea that some mysterious power was enclaved within it. Vassily had not given us away, as David assumed—he wasn't in any state for that; he'd been too badly frightened. It was simply that one of our maids had caught sight of the watch in his hand and had promptly informed our aunt of the fact. And that was the spark that set the whole forest on fire.

So we pelted along the street, right down the very middle. The people in our path stopped or stepped aside, bewildered. I remember how a retired second-major, famous as a hunter with borzois, suddenly leaned out of the window of his lodgings and, crimson in the face, his torso balanced on the sill, gave a fierce "View halloo!" "Stop! Stop!" still thundered after us. David ran on whirling the watch above his head, and giving a skip every now and then; I skipped in the same way, in the same places, as he did.

"Where to?" I shouted to David, seeing him turn out of the street into a side lane, and turning into it after him.

"To the Oka!" he shouted. "Throw it into the water, into the river, to the devil!"

"Stop! Stop!" they were howling behind us.

But already we were flying down the lane. Already we felt fresh chill air—and the river lay before us, and the steep muddy slope; and the wooden bridge, with a train of baggage carts strung out across it, and a garrison-soldier with a pike beside the barrier (in those days, soldiers carried pikes). Now David was on the bridge—and whipping past the soldier, who tried to hit him in the leg with his pike and hit a calf that was walking past. David instantly jumped up onto the parapet; he gave a cry of jubilation. Something white, something blue sparkled, flashed in the air—it was the silver watch with Vassily's glass beads streaking into the waves. But then something incredible happened! After the watch, up shot David's feet, and then his whole body—head first, arms out in front of him, jacket-tails flying apart—described a sharp curve in the air. Thus on a hot day do startled frogs leap from a high bank into the water of a pond. And instantly disappeared beyond the parapet of the bridge. And then—plop— a tremendous splash below.

The effect on me I am powerless, utterly, to describe. I was a few paces away from David when he jumped from the parapet; but I don't even remember whether I cried out; I don't even think I was frightened; I was numbed, I was stupefied. My arms and legs went dead. Around me people were jostling and running. Some of them seemed to be people I knew: Trophimich flashed by; the soldier with the pike rushed somewhere off to the side; the horses of the baggage train crossed over rapidly, their heads jerked back hard. Then everything went green and someone gave me a violent shove on the back of my neck, and all along my back. I had fainted.

I remember I got up presently; and seeing that nobody was paying any attention to me I went to the parapet—but not to the side David had jumped from: it seemed to me dreadful to go there—but to the other, and began to look at the river— turbulent, dark blue, swollen. I remember I noticed a boat moored not far from the bridge, by the shore, and several people in the boat, and one of them, all wet and glistening in the sun, bending over the side, was pulling something out of the water, something not very big, a longish dark object which I took first for a traveling-trunk or a basket; but looking more intently I saw that this object was—David! Then I gave a great start, cried out at the top of my voice, and ran to the boat, pushing through the crowd; and when I'd run up to it, quailed, and began to look around. Among the people clustered about it I recognized Trankvillitatin, the good Agapit, with a shoe in his hand, Yushka, Vassily . . . The shining wet man lugged David's body out of the boat by the armpits. (Both David's hands were up to his face as if he wanted to hide it from the view of strangers.) The man laid him on his back on the riverside mud. David did not stir; he looked as though he had stretched himself out, brought his heels together, and pushed out his stomach. His face was greenish, his eyes had rolled up, water dripped from his hair. The wet man who had pulled him out—a factory hand to judge by his clothes—began to tell how he had done it, shivering with cold and continually pushing his hair back off his forehead. He told the tale very decorously and carefully:

"What in the world do I see, gentlemen? Out of the blue, this lad's off the bridge. Well! Right away I'm downstream at the double, because I know he's fallen right into the current and it'll carry him under the bridge, and, well, it'll be the last of him. . . . I look: there's this shaggy cap, like, floating, but it's his head! So quick and lively I'm in the water and I've raked him out. Anybody could have done it!"

Two or three approving words could be heard in the crowd.

"Better get yourself warmed up now, let's go and have a nip," said someone.

But then someone forced his way convulsively to the front. It was Vassily.

"What's the matter with you all, good Christian people?" he cried tearfully. "We must rock him and bring him to! It's our young gentleman!"

"Rock him, rock him!" resounded in the crowd, which was constantly getting bigger.

"Hold him up by his feet!—that's the right way!"

"Put him over a barrel belly down—and roll him back and forth meanwhile—take him up, boys!"

"Don't you dare touch him," interposed the soldier with the pike. "He has to be hauled off to the guardhouse."

"Scum!" Trophimich's bass voice came from somewhere.

"Why, he's alive!" I shouted all at once at the top of my voice, almost in panic.

I had put my face close to his . . . "So *this* is what drowned men look like!" I thought, and my heart stood still. . . . Then all at once I saw David's lips quiver, and he threw up a little water.

At once they pushed me and pulled me away; they all rushed up to him.

"Rock him, rock him!" voices clamored.

"No, no, stop!" shouted Vassily. "Take him home—home!"

"Home!" Trankvillitatin himself took it up.

"We can have him there in no time, we can see what to do better there," continued Vassily. (From that day on, I loved Vassily.) "Brothers! Isn't there a mat? Or if there isn't take him by his head and feet."

"Wait! Here's a mat! Lay him on it! Pick him up! Let's go! Grand: like riding in a coach!"

And a few minutes later David, borne on the matting, made a ceremonial entrance under our roof again.

20

They undressed him and put him to bed. Already, in the street, he had begun to give signs of life, guggled, and flipped his hands. In the bedroom he came to completely. But as soon as he was no longer in danger of his life and there was no more point in exertions on his behalf, indignation came into its own. Everybody retreated from him as if from a leper.

"God punish him! God punish him!" screeched my aunt so that she could be heard all over the house. "Get rid of him somehow, Porphiry Petrovich, or he'll get us into such trouble we'll never see the end of it!"

"He's a viper, if you ask me, and possessed by a devil too," said her yes-man Trankvillitatin.

"The wickedness of it, the wickedness!" squawked my aunt, coming right to the door of our room so that David should be sure to hear. "First he stole the watch and then he threw it into the water. As much as to say nobody should have it—really!"

Everybody was indignant—everybody.

"David," I asked him as soon as we were left alone. "Why did you do it?"

"There you go, too," he retorted in a voice that was still very weak; his lips were blue and he looked all bloated. "What did I do?"

"Why, why did you jump into the water?"

"Jump! I lost my balance on the parapet, that's the whole story. If I could swim I'd have jumped on purpose. I must certainly learn. Anyway the watch is now—poof!"

But now my father, with solemn step, walked into the room.

"You, my friend"—he turned to me—"I shall flog for certain; make no doubt of that—even if you are too big to lie across a bench any longer." Then he went up to the bed where David lay. "In Siberia," he began in an impressive and consequential tone: "Siberia, my young sir, in penal servitude, in the mines, there are people living and dying who are less guilty, less criminal, than you! Are you a suicide, or a common thief, or simply an utter fool? Tell me that one thing, as a favor!"

"I'm not a suicide, and neither am I a thief," replied David, "but the truth's the truth. There *are* good people in Siberia, better than you or I . . . Who should know that if not you?"

My father gave a little gasp, took a step back, stared at David, spat, and, slowly crossing himself, went out.

"Don't you like that?" David called after him, and stuck out his tongue. Then he tried to get up, but could not. "I must have hurt myself somehow," he said, grunting and corrugating his face. "I remember, the water dashed me against a log . . . Have you seen Raisa?" he added abruptly.

"No, I haven't—Wait! Wait! Wait! Now I remember: wasn't she standing on the shore, by the bridge? Yes . . . a dark dress, a yellow kerchief on her head: it must have been Raisa."

"Well, and afterwards—did you see her?"

"Afterwards . . . I don't know. I wasn't in a state to notice . . . You'd gone and jumped."

David took alarm.

"Alyosha, old friend, go to her right away, tell her I'm all right, there's nothing wrong with me. I'll be at their house tomorrow. Quick as you can, brother, as favor to me!"

David reached both hands out to me. His red hair, dry now, stuck out in comical tufts—but the entendered expression on his face seemed all the more heartfelt for that. I took my cap and left the house, trying not to come in sight of my father and remind him of his promise.

21

"And now that I come to think of it," I wondered, making for the Latkins, "how was it I *didn't* notice Raisa? What became of her? She must have seen—"

And suddenly I remembered: at the very moment of David's fall a terrible rending shriek had rung in my ears.

Hadn't that been she? But how came it I hadn't seen her afterwards?

In front of the little house where Latkin lived there was a patch of wasteland, overgrown with nettles and surrounded by a broken-down fence. I'd hardly got over this fence (there was no gate) when I beheld the following spectacle: On the bottom step of the little porch in front of the house sat Raisa, her elbows on her knees and her chin propped on her intertwined fingers; she was staring blankly ahead of her. Beside her stood her dumb little sister, quite unperturbed, brandishing a little whip. And in front of the porch with his back to me, in a ragged worn-out jacket, long drawers, and felt boots on his feet, old Latkin was mincing and bobbing up and down—jerking his elbows in and out, and writhing. Hearing my footsteps he turned around abruptly, squatted on his heels, and kicking right up to me, began to speak in a quavering and extraordinarily rapid voice with incessant "chu-chu-chu's." I was stupefied. I had not seen him for a long time and should certainly not have recognized him had I met him in another place. That wrinkled, toothless, red face, those round dim little eyes, that disheveled gray hair; these twitchings, these capers, this nonsensical cross-speech: What did it mean? What inhuman despair lacerated this unhappy being? What was this "dance of death"?

"Chu, chu," he chattered without ceasing to writhe. "Vassilyevna there, just now, chu, chu, she came—Hark! with a little trough along the roof" (he clapped himself on the head) "and she sits, so, a shovel, and she is cross-eyed, cross-eyed like Andryushka; Vassilyevna is cross-eyed." (He probably meant: dumb.) "Chu! my cross-eyed Vassilyevna! Look, they're both on the same crust now. Feast your eyes, good Christian people! I have only these two little boats. Ah?"

Latkin was obviously aware that he was speaking all out of kilter, and made terrible efforts to explain to me what the matter was. Raisa apparently didn't hear a thing her father said, and the little sister went on slashing at the air with her whip.

"Goodbye! diamond-merchant, goodbye, goodbye!" Latkin dragged out several times in succession, with low bows, as if rejoicing that at last he had caught hold of an intelligible word.

My head was spinning.

"What does it all mean?" I asked an old woman who was peeping out of a window of the house.

"Why, my little dear," she replied in a sing-song, "they say some man, God knows who, got drowned and she saw it. Well, she took fright or something. She came home all right though. But then she sat down on the porch and from that time to this she's been sitting there like a graven image, makes no difference if you speak to her or not. She's lost *her* speech too, apparently. Oh me, oh my!"

"Goodbye, goodbye," Latkin reiterated, still with the same obeisances.

I went to Raisa and stood directly in front of her.

"Raisa, Raisochka," I exclaimed. "What's the matter with you?"

She made no answer; she did not even seem to notice me. Her face had not turned pale, had not changed—but had somehow gone stony, and the expression on it was as if . . . as if she were just about to fall asleep that instant.

"Yes she's really cross-eyed, cross-eyed," Latkin chattered in my ear.

I took Raisa's hand.

"David's alive," I cried, louder than before; "alive and well; David is alive, do you understand? They pulled him out of the water; he's home now and he told me to say he'll come to see you tomorrow—he's alive!"

As if with difficulty, Raisa raised her eyes to me; she blinked them several times, opening them wider and wider; then she tilted her head to one side and gradually flushed crimson; her lips parted. . . . Slowly she drew a great deep breath of air, grimaced as if in pain, and, having brought out, with a dreadful effort: "Da—Dav—a—live," got up impetuously from the step—and away she shot.

"Where are you going?" I cried.

But laughing a little low laugh, staggering, already she was running across the waste patch.

I set off after her, of course, whilst behind me there arose in unison a senile wail and a childish one, from Latkin and the deaf-and-dumb girl. Raisa sped straight towards our house.

"What a day!" I thought, trying to keep up with the black dress that flashed ahead of me. "Whew!"

22

Just missing Vassily, my aunt, and Trankvillitatin, Raisa ran into the room where David lay and threw herself on his breast.

"Oh—Oh—Da-vey," rang her voice from under her disheveled curls. "Oh!"

With a strong sweep of his arms David hugged her and pressed his head to her.

"Forgive me, my heart"—I could hear his voice too.

And they both seemed to go into a trance of joy.

"But why did you go home, Raisa, why didn't you stay?" I said to her. She still did not lift her head. "You would have seen that they rescued him . . ."

"Ah, I don't know! Ah, I don't know! Don't ask me! I don't know, I don't remember how I got home. I only remember I saw you in the air . . . Something hit me . . . But as to what happened after . . ."

"Something hit you . . ." David repeated. And all three of us together suddenly burst out laughing. We were very happy.

"And what may be the meaning of this, may I ask?" A threatening voice was heard behind us—my father's voice. He was standing in the doorway. "Are these tomfooleries going to end, or not? Where is it we are living—in the Russian Empire, or in the French Republic?"

He came into the room.

"Get out and go to France, anyone who wants to be rebellious and immoral! And you there, how dare *you* come here?" He addressed Raisa, who, quietly straightening up and turning to face him, was evidently a little intimidated but continued to smile a tender beatified smile. "The daughter of my sworn enemy! How could you have the audacity? And your arms around each other, furthermore! Get out of here this instant, or else . . ."

"Uncle!" David said, sitting up in bed. "Don't insult Raisa. She'll go—only don't you insult her!"

"And who are you to be giving me orders? I am not insulting her, not in-sul-ting! but simply turning her out. And I still have an account to settle with *you.* You have done away with other people's property, you have made an attempt on your own life, you have put me to expense . . ."

"What expense?" interrupted David.

"What expense? You've ruined your clothes, do you call that nothing? And then I tipped the men who carried you here. You've given the whole family a fright—and now you're still going to act up? And if this girl here, regardless of modesty and even of her honor . . ."

David jerked himself half out of bed.

"Don't insult her, I tell you!"

"Hold your tongue!"

107

"Don't you dare . . ."

"Hold your tongue!"

"Don't you dare cast aspersions on my fiancée—" shouted David at the top of his lungs "—my future wife!"

"Fiancée!" my father repeated, and his eyes popped. "Fiancée! Wife! Ho, ho, ho!" ("Ha, ha, ha!" echoed my aunt behind the door.) "Why, how old are you? He isn't out of the cradle yet, the milk isn't dry on his lips, he's still in his teens! And he's going to get married! Why I—why you . . ."

"Let me go, let me go," whispered Raisa, and she moved towards the door. She had gone deathly pale.

"I won't be asking permission of you," David went on shouting, propping himself on the edge of the bed with his fists, "but of my own father, who's bound to come any day now! *He* gives me orders, not you; and as far as my age is concerned Raisa and I aren't in any hurry; we'll wait, whatever you may say . . ."

"Eh, David, come to your senses!" my father interrupted. "Just look at yourself. You've . . . all come apart. You've lost all sense of decency."

David caught at the front of his shirt.

"Whatever you may say," he repeated.

"Go on, shut his mouth for him, Porphiry Petrovich, shut his mouth," squeaked my aunt from behind the door. "And as for that trollop, that good-for-nothing girl . . . that—"

But just at that moment something or other out of the ordinary evidently cut my aunt's eloquence short. Her voice broke off abruptly and in its place we heard another, hoarse with old age, and frail.

"Brother!" this feeble voice pronounced. "Fellow Christian!"

23

We all turned. In the same costume I had seen him in just now, like a specter—thin, miserable, and wild—Latkin stood before us.

"God!" he said, like a child somehow, pointing a trembling bent finger upwards and looking at my father with a feeble gaze. "God has punished . . . But I have come for Va—for Ra—yes, yes, for Raisochka! What . . . chu! What does it matter about me? Soon under the ground—and, how's it called now? One little stick, another . . . a cross stick—that's what I . . . need . . . But you, brother diamond-merchant . . . You take care . . . I am a human being too."

Raisa crossed the room mutely and, taking Latkin's arm, she buttoned up his jacket.

"Let's go, Vassilyevna," he said. "Here they're all saints, don't come to their house. That one too, that's lying over there in his case"—he pointed to David—"he's a saint too. But you and I, brother, we are sinners. Well, chu . . . Gentlemen, forgive a peppery old man! We stole *together*!" he cried suddenly. "We stole together! We stole together!" he repeated with manifest delight: his tongue had at last obeyed him.

We were all of us silent in the room.

"But where is your . . . icon?" he asked, throwing his head back and casting up his eyes. "I must purge my soul . . ."

He began to pray towards a corner of the room, crossing himself with unction, tapping his fingers first on one shoulder and then on the other, several times in succession, and hurriedly repeating: "Lord have mercy upon me, Lor'—me, Lor'—me, Lor'!" My father, who all this time had not taken his eyes from Latkin or spoken a word, gave a start and went and stood beside him, and he too began to cross himself. Then he turned to him, bowed low, very low, so that he touched the floor with one hand, and, saying: "And do *you* forgive me too, Martinyan Gavrilich—" kissed him on the shoulder. Latkin for answer smacked his lips in the air and blinked his eyes; it is doubtful that he really comprehended what he was doing. Then my father spoke to all who were in the room: to David, to Raisa, to me.

"Do as you like, act as you think best," he said in a sorrowful and quiet voice; and withdrew.

My aunt tried to make up to him, but he cried out at her, sharp and stern. He was deeply shaken.

"Lord, 'a—Lord, 'a—Lord 'a mercy!" repeated Latkin. "I am a human being."

"Goodbye, Davey," said Raisa, and she left the room too, with the old man.

"I'll be at your house tomorrow," David called after her, and turning his face to the wall whispered: "I'm very tired; now it wouldn't be bad to get some sleep"—and was quiet.

I did not leave our room for a long while. I was in hiding. I could not forget what my father had threatened me with. But my apprehensions proved to be unnecessary. He met me—and said not one word. It was awkward for him too, apparently. However, night soon came—and all grew still in the house.

24

Next morning David got up as if nothing at all had happened, and not long after, on one and the same day, two important events took place: in the morning old Latkin died, and towards evening Uncle Igor came to Ryazan—David's father.

Having sent no preliminary letter, having given no one any forewarning, he came down like a sudden fall of snow upon our heads. My father was uncommonly rattled and did not know what to offer his dear guest, where to have him sit; he dashed about like a man who was out of his mind, fidgeted like one who felt guilty. But my uncle did not seem greatly touched by his brother's bustling solicitude; he would say: "What's *that* for?" or "I don't need a thing." He treated my aunt still more coldly; however, she had not much use for him either; in her eyes he was an atheist, a heretic, a Voltairian. (Actually he *had* learned French in order to read Voltaire in the original.) I found Uncle Igor just as David had described him to me. He was a big heavy man with a broad pock-marked face, dignified and serious. He always wore a plumed hat, lace cuffs and jabot, and a snuff-colored waistcoat, with a steel sword at his side. David was unutterably glad to see him. His face lightened up and became handsome, and his eyes looked different—blithe, quick, and bright—but he did his utmost to modify his rapture and not put it into words; he was afraid of becoming soft. The very first night after Uncle Igor's arrival they both, father and son, shut themselves up in the room he'd been given, and they had a long talk in low voices; next morning I observed that my uncle looked at his son in a particularly affectionate and trustful way; he seemed very much pleased with him.

David took him to the requiem mass for Latkin. I went too; my father did not hinder me, but he himself stayed home. I was struck by Raisa's composure; she was pale and had grown very thin, but she shed no tears and spoke and behaved with great simplicity; but for all that, strange to say, I found a certain majesty in her—the unwilled majesty of grief, which is forgetful of itself! Uncle Igor made her acquaintance right there, on the church porch; but from the way he treated her it was evident that David had already told him about her. He was as pleased with her as with his son; I could read it in David's eyes when he looked at them both. I recollect how they shone when his father said, speaking of her in front of him: "An intelligent girl; she will make a fine woman." At the Latkin's house they told me that the old man had gone out quietly, like a candle burnt down to the end, and that until he lost all power and consciousness he kept stroking his daughter's hair, smiling, and saying something unintelligible but not unhappy. At the funeral, my father went both to the church and to the graveyard, and prayed very fervently. Trankvillitatin sang in the choir. At the grave, Raisa all at once began to sob and fell forward to the ground; she soon recovered, though. Her little sister, deaf and dumb, looked around at everyone and everything with her big gleaming wild eyes; from time to time she would press close up against Raisa, but she gave no signs of being frightened.

On the day after the funeral Uncle Igor, who by all indications had not returned from Siberia empty-handed (*he* provided the money for the funeral, and he rewarded David's rescuer liberally), but who had told us nothing about his life there and had communicated none of his plans for the future—suddenly Uncle Igor notified my father that he did not intend to remain in Ryazan but was going to Moscow with his son. My father, for the sake of decency, expressed regret and even tried—very weakly, it's true—to change my uncle's decision; but deep down, I daresay, he was very glad of it. The presence of a brother with whom he had very little in common, who did not think him even worthy of reproach, who did not even despise, but simply had no stomach for him—oppressed him . . . nor did parting with David constitute any great grief for him. I, of course, was annihilated by this separation. I felt as an orphan might feel, for the first while; I was deprived of what had shored my life up, and lost all interest in living.

And so my uncle went away, and took with him not only David but—to the great amazement and even indignation of our whole street—Raisa and her little sister as well. Learning of this piece of behavior, my aunt promptly dubbed him a Turk, and Turk she called him to the very end of her life.

And I was left alone, alone . . . But the story is not about me.

25

That is the end of my history of the watch. What else is there to tell you? Five years later David married his "Black-lip," and in 1812, as a lieutenant of artillery, he died a glorious death in the Battle of Borodino, defending the Shevardinsky redoubt.

Since that time, much water has flowed by, and I have had many watches: I have even arrived at such grandeur as to own a genuine Breguet with a second hand, a date-indicator, and a repeater. But in a secret drawer of my writing table I keep an old-fashioned silver timepiece with a rose on its face: I bought it from a Jewish peddler, struck by its likeness to the watch my godfather gave me once. From time to time when I am alone and am not expecting anyone I take it out of the drawer and, gazing at it, I remember the days of my youth and the comrade of those days that have passed away and never will return.

Approximations

Mona Simpson

In my family, there were always two people. First, my mother and father. Carol and John.

They danced. Hundreds of evenings at hundreds of parties in their twenties. A thousand times between songs her eyes completely closed when she leaned against him. He looked down at the top of her head; her part gleamed white, under and between the dark hair. He rubbed her back, trying to rouse her, but she became indistinct, blurring against his jacket. He hugged her imperceptibly closer, moving his hand in slower circles on her back, but when he talked it was to someone else over her head. He closed a big hand on her ear.

How do I know this? I don't. But there was a black and white snapshot with my father staring at someone outside the frame. I was looking at the picture when, for some reason, I asked my mother where he was.

I was young, only four years old, and I had no memories of my father. I must have been repeating a question someone else had asked me. My mother was ironing. It was 1960 and all her summer clothes were seersucker and cotton. Her hands stalled over the iron when I asked the question.

"He's gone," she said, not looking at me. The windows were open. A string of hummingbirds moved on the lilac bush outside. "But," she said, gathering her cheeks, "he'll be coming back."

"When?"

For a moment, her mouth wavered, but then her chin snapped back into a straight line and she pushed the iron over the perforated pink and white fabric again.

"I don't know," she said.

So we waited, without mentioning it, for my father. In the meantime, we got used to living alone. Just the two of us.

Other people asked me questions.

"Any news from your Dad?"

"I don't know."

"You must miss him." Other mothers got maternal, pulling me close to their soft, aproned bellies.

For a moment, but only for a moment, I'd let my eyes close. Then I jerked away. "No," I said.

Saturday nights, we went ice-skating. We wore skin-colored tights and matching short dresses made out of stretch fabric. We skated in tight concentrated figures, our necks bent like horses', following the lines of an 8. Then, when the PA system started up, we broke into free skating, wild around the rink. My mother skated up behind me and caught me at the waist.

"This is how you really lose the pounds," she called, slapping her thigh, "skating fast."

I was always behind. Jerry, the pro, did a T-stop to impress my mother, shaving a comet of ice into the air. They skated around together and I had to slow down to wipe the melting water from my face.

When the music stopped, my mother pulled me over to the barrier, where we ran our skate tips into the soft wood. She pointed up to the rows of empty seats. They were maroon, with the plush worn down in the centers.

"See, when you're older, you can bring a boy you're dating here to see you skate. He can watch and think, hey, she's not just another pretty girl, she can really do something."

She peered into my face with a slanted gaze as if, through a crack, she could see what I'd become.

Taking the skates off, on the bench, was all joy. You could walk without carrying your own weight. Your feet and ankles were pure air. The floors were carpeted with rubber mats, red and black, like a checkerboard. In regular shoes, we walked like saints on clouds. The high domed arena was always cold.

The first time we heard from my father was 1963 in the middle of winter. We got a long distance phone call from Las Vegas and it was him.

"We're going to Disneyland!" my mother said, lifting her eyebrows and covering the mouthpiece with her hand.

Into the phone, she said she'd take me out of school. We'd fly to Las Vegas and then the three of us would drive west to Disneyland. I didn't recognize his voice when my mother held out the receiver.

"Hello, Melinda. This is Daddy."

I shrugged at my mother and wouldn't take the phone. "You'll know him when you see him," she whispered.

We waited three days for our summer linen dresses to be dry-cleaned. "It's going to be *hot*," my mother warned. "Scorching," she added with a smile. It was snowing dry powder when we left Illinois. We only saw white outside the airplane window. Halfway there, we changed in the tiny bathroom, from our winter coats to sleeveless dresses and patent leather thongs. It was still cool in the plane but my mother promised it would be hot on the ground.

It was. The air was swirling with dirt. A woman walked across the airport lobby with a scarf tied around her chest; it trailed behind her, coasting on air.

My mother spotted my father in the crowd, and we all pretended I recognized him too. He looked like an ordinary man. His hair was balding in a small circle. He wore tight black slacks, a brown jacket, and black leather, slip-on shoes. His chin stuck out from his face, giving him an eager look.

He had a car parked outside and my mother got into the front seat with him. We passed hotels with bright blue swimming pools and the brown tinge of the sky hung over the water, like a line of dirt on the rim of a sleeve.

My father's apartment was in a pink stucco building. When we walked up with our suitcases, his three roommates were crowded on the porch, leaning on the iron banister. They wore white V-neck T-shirts and thick dark hair pressed out from under them. I hadn't seen men dressed like that before.

"He told us you had long blonde hair."

"You look like your Dad."

"She's prettier than her Dad."

When my father smiled, the gaps between his teeth made him look unintentionally sad, like a jack-o-lantern. He looked down and I felt he was proud of me. He touched my hair. I loved him blindly, the feeling darkening over everything, but it passed.

My mother stepped up to the porch. "Don't you want to introduce me to your friends, too?"

My father introduced each man separately and each man smiled. Then my father gave me a present: a package of six, different-colored cotton headbands. I held it and didn't tear the cellophane open.

My father worked as a waiter in a hotel restaurant. We had dinner there, eating slowly while he worked, watching him balance dishes on the inside of his arm. He sat down with us while my mother was sipping her coffee. He crossed one leg over the other, smoking luxuriously. My mother leaned closer and whispered in my ear.

"When are we going to Disneyland?" I asked, blankly, saying what she said to say but somehow knowing it was wrong.

My father didn't answer me. He looked at my mother and put out his cigarette. That night in the apartment, they fought. My father's roommates closed the doors to their rooms.

"So, when are we going," my mother asked gamely, crossing one leg over the other on a dinette chair.

His shoulders sloped down. "You were late," he said finally. "You were supposed to be here Monday. When you didn't come, I lost the money I'd saved."

"In three days, how? How could you do that?"

"On the tables."

"You, you can't do this to her," my mother said, her voice gathering like a wave.

They sent me outside to the porch. I heard everything, even their breath, through the screen door. There was a box of matches on the ground and I lit them, one by one, scratching them against the concrete and then dropping them in the dirt when the flames came too close to my fingers. Finally it was quiet. My father came out and opened the screen door and I went in.

They set up the living room couch as a bed for me. They both undressed in my father's bedroom. He pulled off his

118

T-shirt and sat on the bed to untie his shoes. My mother looked back at me, over her shoulder, while she unzipped her dress. Finally, she closed the door.

The next morning my father and I got up before my mother. We went to the hotel coffee shop and sat on stools at the counter. I was afraid to ask for anything; I said I wasn't hungry. My father ordered a soft-boiled egg for himself. His eyes caught on the uniformed waitress, the coffee pot tilting from her hand, a purse on the other end of the counter. The egg came in a white coffee cup. He chopped it with the edge of a spoon, asking me if I'd ever tasted a four-minute egg. I ate a spoonful and I loved it. No other egg was ever so good. I told my father how good it was hoping we could share it. But he slid the whole cup down, the spoon in it, without looking at me and signaled the waitress for another egg.

Walking back to the apartment, he kicked sand into the air. There were no lawns in front of the parked trailers, but the sand was raked and bordered with rows of rocks. My father's black slip-on shoes were scuffed. He was holding my hand but not looking at me.

"So we'll go to Disneyland next trip," he said.

"When?"

Suddenly, I wanted dates and plans and the name of a month, not to see Disneyland but to see him. Taking long steps, trying to match his pace, I wanted to say that I didn't care about Disneyland. I dared myself to talk, after one more, two more, three more steps, all the way to the apartment. But I never said it. All I did was hold his hand tighter and tighter.

"I don't know," he said, letting my hand drop when we came to the steps in front of his apartment.

On the plane home, I was holding the package of head-bands in my lap, tracing them through the cellophane. My mother turned away and looked out the window.

"I work," she said finally. "I pay for your school and your books and your skates and your lessons. *And*," she said in a louder whisper, "I pay the rent."

She picked up the package of headbands and then dropped it back on my lap.

"A seventy-nine-cent package of headbands."

It wasn't fair and I knew it.

The next year my mother went back to Las Vegas without me. She and Jerry, the ice-skating pro, got married. She came back without any pictures of the wedding and Jerry moved in with us.

She said she didn't want to bother with a big wedding since it was her second marriage. She wore a dress she already had.

My mother and I spent all that summer in the arena, where Jerry ran an ice-skating school. All day long the air condition-ers hummed like the inside of a refrigerator. Inside the door of my locker was a picture of Peggy Fleming. Inside my mother's was Sonja Henie. In the main office, there were framed pic-tures of Jerry during his days with Holiday On Ice and the Ice Capades. In them, he didn't look like himself. He had short bristly hair and a glamorous smile. His dark figure slithered backward, his arms pointing to two corners of the photograph. The lighting was yellow and false. In one of the pictures it was snowing.

We practiced all summer for the big show in August. The theme was the calendar; the chorus changed from December angels to April bunnies and May tulips. I couldn't get the quick turns in time with the older girls, so I was taken out of the chorus and given a role of my own. After the Easter number was over and the skaters in bunny costumes crowded backstage, I skated fast around the rink, blowing kisses. A second later, the Zamboni* came out to clear the ice. I stood in back before my turn, terrified to go out too early or too late, with the velvet curtain bunched in my hand.

My mother came up behind me every show and gave me a push, saying "now, go" at the right time. I skated completely by instinct. I couldn't see. My eyes blurred under the strong spotlight. But one night, during the Easter dance, my mother was near the stage exit, laughing with Jerry. She kept trying to bend down to tie her laces and he pulled her up, kissing her. Finally, looking over his shoulder, she saw me and quickly mouthed "go." I went out then but it was too late. I heard the Zamboni growling behind me. I tried to run, forgetting how to skate, and fell forward, flat on the ice. My hands burned when I hurried up behind the moving spotlight and I saw that I'd torn my tights. The edges of the hole on my knee were ragged with blood.

I sat down on the ice backstage while the music for my mother's number started up. I knew it by heart. Jerry led my mother in an elementary waltz. She glinted along the ice, shifting her weight from leg to bent leg. Her skates slid out from her body. She was heavier than she had once been. She swayed, moving her head to glance off the eyes of the crowd. Under the slow spotlight, she twirled inside the box of Jerry's arms.

I quit skating after that. When my mother and Jerry went to the rink I stayed home or went out to play with the other kids in the neighborhood. The next year I joined the Girl Scout troop.

---

* **Zamboni.** A large machine that smoothes the ice, making it easier to skate on.

Eventually, my mother stopped taking lessons, too. Then Jerry went to the rink himself every day, like any other man going to a job.

One Saturday, there was a father/daughter breakfast sponsored by my Girl Scout troop. I must have told my mother about it. But by the time the day came, I'd forgotten and I was all dressed in my play clothes to go outside. I was out the front door when my mother caught me.

"Melinda."

"What?"

"Where are you going?"

"The end of the block."

"Don't you remember your Girl Scout breakfast? You have to go in and change."

I didn't want to go. I was already on the driveway, straddling my bike.

"I don't feel like going to that. I'd rather play."

My mother was wearing her housecoat, but she came outside anyway, holding it closed with one hand over her chest.

"He took the day off and he's in there now getting dressed. Now, come on. Go in and put something on."

"No," I said, "I don't want to."

"Won't you do this for me?" she whispered. "He wants to *adopt* you."

We stood there a minute and then the screen door opened.

"Let her go, Carol. She doesn't have to go if she doesn't want to go. It's up to her."

Jerry was standing in the doorway, all dressed up. His hair was combed down and wet from just taking a shower. He was wearing a white turtleneck sweater and a paisley ascot. I felt sorry for him, looking serious and dressed up like that, and I wanted to change my mind and go in but I thought it was too late and I flew off on my bike. None of the other fathers would be wearing ascots anyway, I was thinking.

My father called again when I was ten, to say he wanted to take me to Disneyland. He said he was living in Reno, Nevada, with a new wife. He and my mother bickered a long time on the phone. He wanted to send a plane ticket for me to come alone. My mother said either both of us went or neither. She said she was afraid he would kidnap me. She held out. Finally, they agreed he'd send the money for two tickets.

Around this time, my mother always told me her dreams, which were about things she wanted. A pale blue Lincoln Continental with a cream-colored interior. A swimming pool with night lights and a redwood fence around the yard. A house with a gazebo you couldn't see from the road.

She had already stopped telling Jerry the things she wanted because he tried to get them for her and he made mistakes. He approximated. He bought her the wrong kind of record player for Christmas and he got a dull gold Cadillac, a used car, for her birthday.

Before we went to California, my mother read about something she wanted. A New Sony Portable Color Television. A jewel. She wanted a white one, she was sure it came in white. In the short magazine article she'd clipped out, it said the TVs were available only in Japan until early 1967, next year, but my mother was sure that by the time we went, they would be all over California.

Jerry took us to the airport and he was quiet while we checked on our luggage. When we got onto the plane, we forgot about him. We made plans to get my father to buy us the new Sony. It was this trip's Disneyland. We'd either win it or lose it depending on how we played.

123

At the airport in Los Angeles, we met Velma, my father's new wife. She was a good ten years older and rich; her fingers were full of jewelry and she had on a brown fur coat.

This trip there was no struggle. We went straight to Disneyland. We stayed in the Disneyland Hotel. The four of us went through Disneyland like a rake. There was nothing we didn't see. We ate at restaurants. We bought souvenirs.

But knowing the real purpose of our trip made talking to my father complicated. As I watched my mother laugh with him I was never sure if it was a real laugh, for pleasure, or if it was work, to get our TV. My father seemed sad and a little bumbling. With everyone else around, my father and I didn't talk much.

"How's school?" he asked, walking to the Matterhorn.

"Fine," I said, "I like it."

"That's good," he said.

Our conversations were always like that. It was like lighting single matches.

And I was getting nervous. We were leaving in a day and nothing was being done about the new Sony. The last night, Velma suggested that I meet my father downstairs in the lobby before dinner, so the two of us could talk alone. In our room, my mother brushed my hair out in a fan across my back.

I was nervous. I didn't know what to say to my father.

My mother knew. "See if you can get him to buy the TV," she said. "I bet they've got one for sale right nearby."

I said I hadn't seen any in the stores.

"I think I saw one," she said, winking, "a white one."

"What should I do?" I knew I had to learn everything.

"Tell him you're saving up for it. He'll probably just buy it for you." My mother wasn't nervous. "Suck in your cheeks," she said, brushing glitter on my face. She was having fun.

I didn't want to leave the room. But my mother gave me a short push and I went slowly down the stairs. I tried to remember everything she told me. *Chin up. Smile. Brush your hair back. Say you're saving for it. Suck in your cheeks.* It seemed I was on the verge of losing one of two things I badly wanted. With each step it seemed I was choosing.

I saw my father's back first. He was standing by the candy counter. Whenever I saw my father I went through a series of gradual adjustments, like when you step out of the ice rink, in summer, and feel the warm air. I had to focus my vision down from an idea as vague as a color, to him. He was almost bald. The way his chin shot out made him always look eager. He was buying a roll of Life Savers.

"Would you like anything?" he asked, seeing me and tilting his head to indicate the rows of candy arranged on the counter.

I thought for a wild moment. I could give up the plan, smile and say yes. Yes I want a candy bar. Two candy bars. He'd buy me two of the best candy bars there. I could stand and eat them sloppily, all the while gazing up at my father. If I smiled, he would smile. He would bend down and dab the chocolate from my mouth with a handkerchief moist with his own saliva.

But I didn't say yes, because I knew it would end. I knew I'd remember my father's face, soft on mine, next year when no letters came. I would hate my best memory because it would prove that my father could fake love or that love could end or, worst of all, that love was not powerful enough to change a life, his life.

"No," I said, "I'm saving up my money."

"What?" he said, smiling down at me. He was unraveling the paper from his Life Savers.

I gulped. "I'm saving my money for a new Sony portable color television," I said.

He scanned the drugstore for a moment. I think we both knew he was relinquishing me to my mother.

"Oh," he said finally, nodding.

We didn't get the Sony. On the way home, neither of us mentioned it. And when the plane landed, we didn't call Jerry. We took a taxi from the airport. When we got home, my mother collapsed on the blue-green couch and looked around the room disapprovingly. The suitcases were scattered on the floor.

"You didn't say one big word the whole time we were there," she said. "Here, you're clever. You should hear yourself kidding around with Jerry. You say three syllable words and . . . There, you didn't say one smart thing in front of him. Let me tell you, you sounded dumb."

She imitated a dumb person, stretching her eyes wide open and puffing air into her cheeks.

She sighed. "Go out and play," she said. "Go out and play with your friends."

But I just stood there looking at her. She got worse. She kicked off her shoes. She began throwing pillows from the couch onto the floor.

"Not one big word. The whole time we were there," she said.

"And you didn't smile. Here, you're sharp, you're animate. There you slumped. You looked down. You really just looked ordinary. Like any other kid around here. Well, it's a good thing we're back because I can see now this is just where you belong. With all the mill workers' kids. Well, here we are. Good."

She was still yelling when I walked out the door. Then I did something I'd never done before. I walked down to the end of our road and I hitchhiked. I got picked up by a lady

126

who lived two blocks away. I told her I was going to the arena.

From the lobby I saw Jerry on the ice. I ran downstairs to my mother's locker and sat alone, lacing up skates. I ran up the hall on my skate points and I ran onto the ice fast, my arms straight out to the sides. I went flying toward Jerry.

He was bending over a woman's shoulders, steering her into a figure eight.

A second later he saw me and I was in his arms, breathing against the wool of his sweater. He put a hand over my ear and told his student something I couldn't understand.

A few seconds later, when I pulled myself away, the student was gone. I stopped crying and then there was nothing to do. We were alone on the ice.

I looked up at Jerry; it was different than with my father. I couldn't bury my face in Jerry's sweater and forget the world. I stood there nervously. Jerry was still Jerry, standing in front of me shyly, a man I didn't know. My father was gone for good and here was Jerry, just another man in the world, who had nothing to do with me.

"Would you like me to teach you to do loops?" he asked quietly.

I couldn't say no because of how he looked, standing there with his hands in his pockets.

I glanced up at the empty stands around us. I was tired. And cold. Jerry started skating in tight, precise loops. I looked down at the lines he was making on the ice.

"I'll try," I said, beginning to follow them.

THE GRIFFIN AND THE MINOR CANON

Frank R. Stockton

Over the great door of an old, old church, which stood in a quiet town of a faraway land, there was carved in stone the figure of a large griffin. The old-time sculptor had done his work with great care, but the image he had made was not a pleasant one to look at. It had a large head, with enormous open mouth and savage teeth; from its back arose great wings, armed with sharp hooks and prongs; it had stout legs in front, with projecting claws; but there were no legs behind—the body, running out into a long and powerful tail, finished off at the end with a barbed point. This tail was coiled up under it, the end sticking up just behind its wings.

The sculptor, or the people who had ordered his stone figure, had evidently been very much pleased with it, for little copies of it, also in stone, had been placed here and there along the sides of the church not very far from the ground, so that people could easily look at them and ponder on their curious forms. There were a great many other sculptures on the outside of this church—saints, martyrs, grotesque heads of men, beasts, and birds, as well as those of other creatures which cannot be named, because nobody knows exactly what they were—but none were so curious and interesting as the great griffin over the door and the little griffins on the sides of the church.

A long, long distance from town, in the midst of dreadful wilds scarcely known to man, there dwelt the Griffin whose image had been put up over the church door. In some way or other, the old-time sculptor had seen him, and afterward, to the best of his memory, had copied his figure in stone. The Griffin had never known this until, hundreds of years afterward, he heard from a bird, from a wild animal, or in some manner which it is not now easy to find out, that there was a likeness of him on the old church in the distant town.

Now, this Griffin had no idea how he looked. He had never seen a mirror, and the streams where he lived were so turbulent and violent that a quiet piece of water, which would reflect the image of anything looking into it, could not be found. Being, as far as could be ascertained, the very last of his race, he had never seen another griffin. Therefore it was that when he heard of this stone image of himself, he became very anxious to know what he looked like and at last determined to go to the old church and see for himself what manner of being he was. So he started off from the dreadful wilds, and flew on and on until he came to the countries inhabited by men, where his appearance in the air created great consternation; but he alighted nowhere, keeping up a steady flight until he reached the suburbs of the town which had his image on its church. Here, late in the afternoon, he alighted in a green meadow by the side of a brook and stretched himself on the grass to rest. His great wings were tired, for he had not made such a long flight in a century or more.

The news of his coming spread quickly over the town, and the people, frightened nearly out of their wits by the arrival of so extraordinary a visitor, fled into their houses and shut themselves up. The Griffin called loudly for someone to come to him, but the more he called, the more afraid the people were to show themselves. At length, he saw two laborers hurrying to their homes through the fields, and in a terrible voice he commanded them to stop. Not daring to disobey, the men stood, trembling.

"What is the matter with you all?" cried the Griffin. "Is there not a man in your town who is brave enough to speak to me?"

"I think," said one of the laborers, his voice shaking so that his words could hardly be understood, "that—perhaps—the Minor Canon—would come."

"Go, call him then!" said the Griffin. "I want to see him."

The Minor Canon, who filled a subordinate position in the old church, had just finished the afternoon services and was coming out of the church with three aged women who had formed the weekday congregation. He was a young man of a kind disposition, and very anxious to do good to the people of the town. Apart from his duties in the church, where he conducted services every weekday, he visited the sick and the poor, counseled and assisted persons who were in trouble, and taught a school composed entirely of the bad children in the town with whom nobody else would have anything to do. Whenever the people wanted something difficult done for them, they always went to the Minor Canon. Thus it was that the laborer thought of the young priest when he found that someone must come and speak to the Griffin.

The Minor Canon had not heard of the strange event, which was known to the whole town except himself and the three old women, and when he was informed of it and was told that the Griffin had asked to see him, he was greatly amazed and frightened.

"Me!" he exclaimed. "He has never heard of me! What should he want with me?"

"Oh, you must go instantly!" cried the two men. "He is very angry now because he has been kept waiting so long, and nobody knows what may happen if you don't hurry to him."

The poor Minor Canon would rather have had his hand cut off than go out to meet an angry griffin; but he felt that it was his duty to go, for it would be a woeful thing if injury should come to the people of the town because he was not brave enough to obey the summons of the Griffin. So, pale and frightened, he started off.

"Well," said the Griffin, as soon as the young man came nearer, "I am glad to see that there is someone who has the courage to come to me."

The Minor Canon did not feel very courageous, but he bowed his head.

"Is this the town," said the Griffin, "where there is a church with a likeness of myself over one of the doors?"

The Minor Canon looked at the frightful creature before him and saw that he was, without doubt, exactly like the stone image on the church. "Yes," he said, "you are right."

"Well, then," said the Griffin, "will you take me to it? I wish very much to see it."

The Minor Canon instantly thought that if the Griffin entered the town without the people knowing what he came for, some of them would probably be frightened to death, and so he sought to gain time to prepare their minds.

"It is growing dark now," he said, very much afraid, as he spoke, that his words might enrage the Griffin, "and objects on the front of the church cannot be seen clearly. It will be better to wait until morning, if you wish to get a good view of the stone image of yourself."

"That will suit me very well," said the Griffin. "I see you are a man of good sense. I am tired, and I will take a nap here on this soft grass while I cool my tail in the little stream that runs near me. The end of my tail gets red-hot when I am angry or excited, and it is quite warm now. So you may go; but be sure and come early tomorrow morning and show me the way to the church."

The Minor Canon was glad enough to take his leave, and hurried into the town. In front of the church he found a great many people assembled to hear his report of his interview with the Griffin. When they found that the creature had not come to spread ruin and devastation, but simply to see his stony likeness on the church, they showed neither relief nor gratification, but began to upbraid the Minor Canon for consenting to conduct the creature into the town.

"What could I do?" cried the young man. "If I should not bring him, he would come himself, and perhaps end by setting fire to the town with his red-hot tail."

Still the people were not satisfied, and a great many plans were proposed to prevent the Griffin from coming into the town. Some elderly persons urged that the young men should go out and kill him; but the young men scoffed at such a ridiculous idea. Then someone said that it would be a good thing to destroy the stone image so that the Griffin would have no excuse for entering the town; and this proposal was received with such favor that many of the people ran for hammers, chisels, and crowbars, with which to tear down and break up the stone griffin. But the Minor Canon resisted this plan with all the strength of his mind and body. He assured the people that this action would enrage the Griffin beyond measure, for it would be impossible to conceal from him that his image had been destroyed during the night. But the people were so determined to break up the stone griffin that the Minor Canon saw that there was nothing for him to do but to stay there and protect it. All night he walked up and down in front of the church door, keeping away the men who brought ladders by which they might mount to the great stone griffin and knock it to pieces with their hammers and crowbars. After many hours, the people were obliged to give up their attempts and went home to sleep; but the Minor Canon remained at his post till early morning, and then he hurried away to the field where he had left the Griffin.

The monster had just awakened, and rising to his forelegs and shaking himself, he said that he was ready to go into the town. The Minor Canon therefore walked back, the Griffin flying slowly through the air at a short distance above the head of his guide. Not a person was to be seen in the streets, and they proceeded directly to the front of the church, where the Minor Canon pointed out the stone griffin.

The real Griffin settled down in the little square before the church and gazed earnestly at his sculptured likeness. For a long time he looked at it. First he put his head on one side, and then he put it on the other; then he shut his right eye and gazed with his left, after which he shut his left eye and gazed with his right. Then he moved a little to one side and looked at the image, then he moved the other way. After a while he said to the Minor Canon, who had been standing by all this time, "It is, it must be, an excellent likeness! That breadth between the eyes, that expansive forehead, those massive jaws! I feel that it must resemble me. If there is any fault to find with it, it is that the neck seems a little stiff. But that is nothing. It is an admirable likeness—admirable!"

The Griffin sat looking at his image all the morning and all the afternoon. The Minor Canon had been afraid to go away and leave him, and had hoped all through the day that he would soon be satisfied with his inspection and fly away home. But by evening, the poor young man was utterly exhausted and felt that he must eat and sleep. He frankly admitted this fact to the Griffin and asked him if he would not like something to eat. He said this because he felt obliged in politeness to do so, but as soon as he had spoken the words, he was seized with dread lest the monster should demand half-a-dozen babies or some tempting repast of that kind.

"Oh, no," said the Griffin. "I never eat between the equinoxes. At the vernal and at the autumnal equinox I take a good meal, and that lasts me for half a year. I am extremely regular in my habits and do not think it healthful to eat at odd times. But if you need food, go and get it, and I will return to the soft grass where I slept last night and take another nap."

The next day, the Griffin came again to the little square before the church and remained there until evening, stead-fastly regarding the stone griffin over the door. The Minor Canon came once or twice to look at him, and the Griffin seemed very glad to see him; but the young clergyman could not stay as he had done before, for he had many duties to perform. Nobody went to the church, but the people came to the Minor Canon's house and anxiously asked him how long the Griffin was going to stay.

"I do not know," he answered, "but I think he will soon be satisfied with regarding his stone likeness and then he will go away."

But the Griffin did not go away. Morning after morning he came to the church, but after a time he did not stay there all day. He seemed to have taken a great fancy to the Minor Canon, and followed him about as he pursued his various avocations. He would wait for him at the side door of the church, for the Minor Canon held services every day, morning and evening, though nobody came now.

"If anyone should come," he said to himself, "I must be found at my post."

When the young man came out, the Griffin would accompany him on his visits to the sick and the poor, and would often look into the windows of the schoolhouse where the Minor Canon was teaching his unruly scholars. All the other schools were closed, but the parents of the Minor Canon's scholars forced them to go to school, because they were so bad they could not endure them all day at home—Griffin or no Griffin. But it must be said they generally behaved very well when that great monster sat up on his tail and looked in at the schoolroom window.

When it was perceived that the Griffin showed no signs of going away, all the people who were able to do so left the town. The canons and the higher officers of the church had fled away during the first day of the Griffin's visit, leaving behind only the Minor Canon and some of the men who opened the doors and swept the church. All the citizens who could afford it shut up their houses and traveled to distant parts, and only the working people and the poor were left behind. After some days, these ventured to go about and attend to their business, for if they did not work, they would starve. They were getting a little used to seeing the Griffin, and having been told that he did not eat between equinoxes, they did not feel so much afraid of him as before.

Day by day, the Griffin became more and more attached to the Minor Canon. He kept near him a great part of the time and often spent the night in front of the little house where the young clergyman lived alone. This strange companionship was often burdensome to the Minor Canon; but, on the other hand, he could not deny that he derived a great deal of benefit and instruction from it. The Griffin had lived for hundreds of years and had seen much, and he told the Minor Canon many wonderful things.

"It is like reading an old book," said the young clergyman to himself; "but how many books I would have had to read before I would have found out what the Griffin has told me about the earth, the air, the water, about minerals, and metals, and growing things, and all the wonders of the world!"

Thus the summer went on and drew toward its close. And now the people of the town began to be very much troubled again.

"It will not be long," they said, "before the autumnal equinox is here, and then that monster will want to eat. He will be dreadfully hungry, for he has taken so much exercise since his last meal. He will devour our children. Without doubt, he will eat them all. What is to be done?"

To this question no one could give an answer, but all agreed that the Griffin must not be allowed to remain until the approaching equinox. After talking over the matter a great deal, a crowd of the people went to the Minor Canon at a time when the Griffin was not with him.

"It is all your fault," they said, "that that monster is among us. You brought him here, and you ought to see that he goes away. It is only on your account that he stays here at all, for, although he visits his image every day, he is with you the greater part of the time. If you were not here, he would not stay. It is your duty to go away and then he will follow you, and we shall be free from the dreadful danger which hangs over us."

"Go away!" cried the Minor Canon, greatly grieved at being spoken to in such a way. "Where shall I go? If I go to some other town, shall I not take this trouble there? Have I a right to do that?"

"No," said the people, "you must not go to any other town. There is no town far enough away. You must go to the dreadful wilds where the Griffin lives; and then he will follow you and stay there."

They did not say whether or not they expected the Minor Canon to stay there also, and he did not ask them anything about it. He bowed his head and went into his house to think. The more he thought, the more clear it became to his mind that it was his duty to go away and thus free the town from the presence of the Griffin.

That evening, he packed a leather bag full of bread and meat, and early the next morning he set out on his journey to the dreadful wilds. It was a long, weary, and doleful journey, especially after he had gone beyond the habitations of men, but the Minor Canon kept on bravely and never faltered. The way was longer than he had expected, and his provisions soon grew so scanty that he was obliged to eat but a little every day, but he kept up his courage and pressed on, and, after many days of toilsome travel, he reached the dreadful wilds.

When the Griffin found that the Minor Canon had left the town, he seemed sorry, but showed no disposition to go and look for him. After a few days had passed, he became much annoyed and asked some of the people where the Minor Canon had gone. But, although the citizens had been so anxious that the young clergyman should go to the dreadful wilds, thinking that the Griffin would immediately follow him, they were now afraid to mention the Minor Canon's destination, for the monster seemed angry already, and, if he should suspect their trick, he would doubtless become very much enraged. So every one said he did not know, and the Griffin wandered about disconsolate. One morning he looked into the Minor Canon's schoolhouse, which was always empty now, and thought that it was a shame that everything should suffer on account of the young man's absence.

"It does not matter so much about the church," he said, "for nobody went there; but it is a pity about the school. I think I will teach it myself until he returns."

It was the hour for opening the school, and the Griffin went inside and pulled the rope which rang the school bell. Some of the children who heard the bell ran in to see what was the matter, supposing it to be a joke of one of their companions; but when they saw the Griffin they stood astonished and scared.

"Go tell the other scholars," said the monster, "that school is about to open, and that if they are not all here in ten minutes I shall come after them."

In seven minutes, every scholar was in place.

Never was seen such an orderly school. Not a boy or girl moved or uttered a whisper. The Griffin climbed into the master's seat, his wide wings spread on each side of him, because he could not lean back in his chair while they stuck out behind, and his great tail coiled around in front of the desk, the barbed end sticking up ready to tap any boy or girl who might misbehave.

The Griffin now addressed the scholars, telling them that he intended to teach them while their master was away. In speaking, he tried to imitate, as far as possible, the mild and gentle tones of the Minor Canon; but it must be admitted that in this he was not very successful. He had paid a good deal of attention to the studies of the school, and he determined not to try to teach them anything new, but to review them in what they had been studying; so he called up the various classes and questioned them upon their previous lessons. The children racked their brains to remember what they had learned. They were so afraid of the Griffin's displeasure that they recited as they had never recited before. One of the boys, far down in his class, answered so well that the Griffin was astonished.

"I should think you would be at the head," said he. "I am sure you have never been in the habit of reciting so well. Why is this?"

"Because I did not choose to take the trouble," said the boy, trembling in his boots. He felt obliged to speak the truth, for all the children thought that the great eyes of the Griffin could see right through them, and that he would know when they told a falsehood.

"You ought to be ashamed of yourself," said the Griffin. "Go down to the very tail of the class; and if you are not at the head in two days, I shall know the reason why."

The next afternoon this boy was Number One.

It was astonishing how much these children now learned of what they had been studying. It was as if they had been educated over again. The Griffin used no severity toward them, but there was a look about him which made them unwilling to go to bed until they were sure they knew their lessons for the next day.

The Griffin now thought that he ought to visit the sick and the poor; and he began to go about the town for this purpose. The effect upon the sick was miraculous. All, except those who were very ill indeed, jumped from their beds when they heard he was coming, and declared themselves quite well. To those who could not get up, he gave herbs and roots, which none of them had ever before thought of as medicines, but which the Griffin had seen used in various parts of the world; and most of them recovered. But, for all that, they afterward said that no matter what happened to them, they hoped that they should never again have such a doctor coming to their bedsides, feeling their pulses and looking at their tongues.

As for the poor, they seemed to have utterly disappeared. All those who had depended upon charity for their daily bread were now at work in some way or other, many of them offering to do odd jobs for their neighbors just for the sake of their meals—a thing which before had been seldom heard of in the town. The Griffin could find no one who needed his assistance.

The summer had now passed, and the autumnal equinox was rapidly approaching. The citizens were in a state of great alarm and anxiety. The Griffin showed no signs of going away, but seemed to have settled himself permanently among them. In a short time the day for his semiannual meal would arrive, and then what would happen? The monster would certainly be very hungry, and would devour all their children.

Now, they greatly regretted and lamented that they had sent away the Minor Canon; he was the only one on whom they could have depended in this trouble, for he could talk freely with the Griffin and so find out what could be done. But it would not do to be inactive. Some step must be taken immediately. A meeting of the citizens was called, and two old men were appointed to go and talk to the Griffin. They were instructed to offer to prepare a splendid dinner for him on equinox day—one which would entirely satisfy his hunger. They would offer him the fattest mutton, the most tender beef, fish and game of various sorts, and anything of the kind that he might fancy. If none of these suited, they were to mention that there was an orphan asylum in the next town.

"Anything would be better," said the citizens, "than to have our dear children devoured."

The old men went to the Griffin; but their propositions were not received with favor.

"From what I have seen of the people of this town," said the monster, "I do not think I could relish anything which was prepared by them. They appear to be all cowards, and therefore, mean and selfish. As for eating one of them, old or young, I could not think of it for a moment. In fact, there was only one creature in the whole place for whom I could have had any appetite, and that was the Minor Canon, who has gone away. He was brave and good and honest, and I think I should have relished him."

"Ah!" said one of the old men very politely, "in that case I wish we had not sent him to the dreadful wilds!"

"What!" cried the Griffin. "What do you mean? Explain instantly what you are talking about!"

The old man, terribly frightened at what he had said, was obliged to tell how the Minor Canon had been sent away by the people, in the hope that the Griffin might be induced to follow him.

When the monster heard this, he became furiously angry. He dashed away from the old men, and, spreading his wings, flew backward and forward over the town. He was so much excited that his tail became red-hot and glowed like a meteor against the evening sky. When at last he settled down in the little field where he usually rested and thrust his tail into the brook, the steam arose like a cloud and the water of the stream ran hot through the town. The citizens were greatly frightened, and bitterly blamed the old man for telling the Griffin about the Minor Canon.

"It is plain," they said, "that the Griffin intended at last to go and look for him, and we should have been saved. Now, who can tell what misery you have brought upon us?"

The Griffin did not remain long in the little field. As soon as his tail was cool, he flew to the town hall and rang the bell. The citizens knew that they were expected to come there; and although they were afraid to go, they were still more afraid to stay away, and they crowded into the hall. The Griffin was on the platform at one end, flapping his wings and walking up and down, and the end of his tail was still so warm that it slightly scorched the boards as he dragged it after him.

When everybody who was able to come was there, the Griffin stood still and addressed the meeting.

"I have had a very low opinion of you," he said, "ever since I discovered what cowards you are, but I had no idea that you were so ungrateful, selfish, and cruel as I now find you to be. Here was your Minor Canon, who labored day and night for your good, and thought of nothing else but how he might benefit you and make you happy; and as soon as you imagine yourselves threatened with a danger—for well I know you are dreadfully afraid of me—you send him off, caring not whether he returns or perishes, hoping thereby to save yourselves. Now, I had conceived a great liking for that young man, and had intended, in a day or two, to go and look him up. But I have changed my mind about him. I shall go and find him, but I shall send him back here to live among you, and I intend that he shall enjoy the reward of his labor and his sacrifices.

"Go, some of you, to the officers of the church, who were so cowardly as to run away when I first came here, and tell them never to return to this town under penalty of death. And if, when your Minor Canon comes back to you, you do not bow yourselves before him, put him in the highest place among you, and serve and honor him all his life, beware of my terrible vengeance! There were only two good things in this town: the Minor Canon and the stone image of myself over your church door. One of these you have sent away, and the other I shall carry away myself."

With these words he dismissed the meeting; and it was time, for the end of his tail had become so hot that there was danger of its setting fire to the building.

The next morning the Griffin came to the church, and tearing the stone image of himself from its fastenings over the great door, he grasped it with his powerful forelegs and flew up into the air. Then, after hovering over the town for a moment, he gave his tail an angry shake and took up his flight to the dreadful wilds. When he reached this desolate region, he set the stone griffin upon a ledge of a rock which rose in front of the dismal cave he called his home. There, the image occupied a position somewhat similar to that it had had over the church door; and the Griffin, panting with the exertion of carrying such an enormous load so great a distance, lay down upon the ground and regarded it with much satisfaction. When he felt somewhat rested, he went to look for the Minor Canon. He found the young man, weak and half-starved, lying under the shadow of a rock. After picking him up and carrying him to his cave, the Griffin flew away to a distant marsh, where he procured some roots and herbs which he well knew were strengthening and beneficial to man, though he had never tasted them himself. After eating these, the Minor Canon was greatly revived, and sat up and listened while the Griffin told him what had happened in the town.

"Do you know," said the monster, when he had finished, "that I have had, and still have, a great liking for you?"

"I am very glad to hear it," said the Minor Canon, with his usual politeness.

"I am not at all sure that you would be," said the Griffin, "if you thoroughly understood the state of the case; but we will not consider that now. If some things were different, other things would be otherwise. I have been so enraged by discovering the manner in which you have been treated, that I have determined that you shall at last enjoy the rewards and honors to which you are entitled. Lie down and have a good sleep, and then I will take you back to the town."

As he heard these words, a look of trouble came over the young man's face.

"You need not give yourself any anxiety," said the Griffin, "about my return to the town. I shall not remain there. Now that I have that admirable likeness of myself in front of my cave, where I can sit at my leisure and gaze upon its noble features, I have no wish to see that abode of cowardly and selfish people."

The Minor Canon, relieved from his fears, lay back and dropped into a doze; and when he was sound asleep, the Griffin took him up and carried him back to the town. He arrived just before daybreak, and, putting the young man gently on the grass in the little field where he himself used to rest, the monster, without having been seen by any of the people, flew back to his home.

When the Minor Canon made his appearance in the morning among the citizens, the enthusiasm and cordiality with which he was received were truly wonderful. He was taken to a house which had been occupied by one of the banished high officers of the place, and everyone was anxious to do all that could be done for his health and comfort. The people crowded into the church when he held services, so that the three old women who used to be his weekday congregation could not get to the best seats, which they had always been in the habit of taking; and the parents of the bad children determined to reform them at home, in order that he might be spared the trouble of keeping up his former school. The Minor Canon was appointed to the highest office of the old church, and before he died, he became a bishop.

During the first years after his return from the dreadful wilds, the people of the town looked up to him as a man to whom they were bound to do honor and reverence; but they often, also, looked up to the sky to see if there were any signs of the Griffin coming back. However, in the course of time, they learned to honor and reverence their former Minor Canon without the fear of being punished if they did not do so.

But they need never have been afraid of the Griffin. The autumnal equinox came round, and the monster ate nothing. If he could not have the Minor Canon, he did not care for anything. So, lying down, with his eyes fixed upon the great stone griffin, he gradually declined and died. It was a good thing for some of the people of the town that they did not know this.

If you should ever visit the old town, you would still see the little griffins on the sides of the church; but the great stone griffin that was over the door is gone.

STAR FOOD

Ethan Canin

The summer I turned eighteen I disappointed both my parents for the first time. This hadn't happened before, since what disappointed one usually pleased the other. As a child, if I played broom hockey instead of going to school, my mother wept and my father took me outside later to find out how many goals I had scored. On the other hand, if I spent Saturday afternoon on the roof of my parents' grocery store staring up at the clouds instead of counting cracker cartons in the stockroom, my father took me to the back to talk about work and discipline, and my mother told me later to keep looking for things that no one else saw.

This was her theory. My mother felt that men like Leonardo da Vinci and Thomas Edison had simply stared long enough at regular objects until they saw new things, and thus my looking into the sky might someday make me a great man. She believed I had a worldly curiosity. My father believed I wanted to avoid stock work.

146

Stock work was an issue in our family, as were all the jobs that had to be done in a grocery store. Our store was called Star Food and above it an incandescent star revolved. Its circuits buzzed, and its yellow points, as thick as my knees, drooped with the slow melting of the bulb. On summer nights flying insects flocked in clouds around it, droves of them burning on the glass. One of my jobs was to go out on the roof, the sloping, eaved side that looked over the western half of Arcade, California, and clean them off the star. At night, when their black bodies stood out against the glass, when the wind carried in the marsh smell of the New Jerusalem River, I went into the attic, crawled out the dormer window onto the peaked roof, and slid across the shingles to where the pole rose like a lightning rod into the night. I reached with a wet rag and rubbed away the June bugs and pickerel moths until the star was yellow-white and steaming from the moisture. Then I turned and looked over Arcade, across the bright avenue and my dimly lighted high school in the distance, into the low hills where oak trees grew in rows on the curbs and where girls drove to school in their own convertibles. When my father came up on the roof sometimes to talk about the store, we fixed our eyes on the red tile roofs or the small clouds of blue barbecue smoke that floated above the hills on warm evenings. While the clean bulb buzzed and flickered behind us, we talked about loss leaders or keeping the elephant-ear plums stacked in neat triangles.

The summer I disappointed my parents, though, my father talked to me about a lot of other things. He also made me look in the other direction whenever we were on the roof together, not west to the hills and their clouds of barbecue smoke, but east toward the other part of town. We crawled up one slope of the roof, then down the other so I could see beyond the back alley where wash hung on lines in the moonlight, down to the neighborhoods across Route 5. These were the neighborhoods where men sat on the curbs on weekday afternoons, where rusted, wheel-less cars lay on blocks in the yards.

"*You're* going to end up on one of those curbs," my father told me.

Usually I stared farther into the clouds when he said something like that. He and my mother argued about what I did on the roof for so many hours at a time, and I hoped that by looking closely at the amazing borders of clouds I could confuse him. My mother believed I was on the verge of discovering something atmospheric, and I was sure she told my father this, so when he came upstairs, made me look across Route 5, and talked to me about how I was going to end up there, I squinted harder at the sky.

"You don't fool me for a second," he said.

He was up on the roof with me because I had been letting someone steal from the store.

From the time we first had the star on the roof, my mother believed her only son was destined for limited fame. Limited because she thought that true vision was distilled and could not be appreciated by everybody. I discovered this shortly after the star was installed, when I spent an hour looking out over the roofs and chimneys instead of helping my father stock a shipment of dairy. It was a hot day and the milk sat on the loading dock while he searched for me in the store and in our apartment next door. When he came up and found me, his neck was red and his footfalls shook the roof joists. At my age I was still allowed certain mistakes, but I'd seen the dairy truck arrive and knew I should have been downstairs, so it surprised me later, after I'd helped unload the milk, when my mother stopped beside me as I was sprinkling the leafy vegetables with a spray bottle.

"Dade, I don't want you to let anyone keep you from what you ought to be doing."

"I'm sorry," I said. "I should have helped with the milk earlier."

"No," she said, "that's not what I mean." Then she told me her theory of limited fame while I sprayed the cabbage and lettuce with the atomizer. It was the first time I had heard her idea. The world's most famous men, she said, presidents and emperors, generals and patriots, were men of vulgar fame, men who ruled the world because their ideas were obvious and could be understood by everybody. But there was also limited fame. Newton and Galileo and Enrico Fermi were men of limited fame, and as I stood there with the atomizer in my hands my mother's eyes watered over and she told me she knew in her heart that one day I was going to be a man of limited fame. I was twelve years old.

After that day I found I could avoid a certain amount of stock work by staying up on the roof and staring into the fine layers of stratus clouds that floated above Arcade. In the *Encyclopedia Americana* I read about cirrus and cumulus and thunderheads, about inversion layers and currents like the currents at sea, and in the afternoons I went upstairs and watched. The sky was a changing thing, I found out. It was more than a blue sheet. Twirling with pollen and sunlight, it began to transform itself.

Often as I stood on the roof my father came outside and swept the sidewalk across the street. Through the telephone poles and crossed power lines he looked up at me, his broom strokes small and fierce as if he were hoeing hard ground. It irked him that my mother encouraged me to stay on the roof. He was a short man with direct habits and an understanding of how to get along in the world, and he believed that God rewarded only two things, courtesy and hard work. God did

not reward looking at the sky. In the car my father acknowl-
edged good drivers and in restaurants he left good tips. He
knew the names of his customers. He never sold a rotten
vegetable. He shook hands often, looked everyone in the eye,
and on Friday nights when we went to the movies he made us
sit in the front row of the theater. "Why should I pay to look
over other people's shoulders?" he said. The movies made him
talk. On the way back to the car he walked with his hands
clasped behind him and greeted everyone who passed. He
smiled. He mentioned the fineness of the evening as if he
were the admiral or aviator we had just seen on the screen.
"People like it," he said. "It's good for business." My mother
was quiet, walking with her slender arms folded in front of
her as if she were cold.

I liked the movies because I imagined myself doing
everything the heroes did—deciding to invade at daybreak,
swimming half the night against the seaward current—but
whenever we left the theater I was disappointed. From the
front row, life seemed like a clear set of decisions, but on the
street afterward I realized that the world existed all around
me and I didn't know what I wanted. The quiet of evening
and the ordinariness of human voices startled me.

Sometimes on the roof, as I stared into the layers of horizon, the sounds on the street faded into this same ordinariness. One afternoon when I was standing under the star my
father came outside and looked up to me. "You're in a trance,"
he called. I glanced down at him, then squinted back at the
horizon. For a minute he waited, and then from across the
street he threw a rock. He had a pitcher's arm and could have
hit me if he wanted, but the rock sailed past me and clattered
on the shingles. My mother came right out of the store
anyway and stopped him. "I wanted him off the roof," I heard
my father tell her later in the same frank voice in which he

explained his position to vegetable salesmen. "If someone's throwing rocks at him he'll come down. He's no fool."

I was flattered by this, but my mother won the point and from then on I could stay up on the roof when I wanted. To appease my father I cleaned the electric star, and though he often came outside to sweep, he stopped telling me to come down. I thought about limited fame and spent a lot of time noticing the sky. When I looked closely it was a sea with waves and shifting colors, wind seams and denials of distance, and after a while I learned to look at it so that it entered my eye whole. It was blue liquid. I spent hours looking into its pale wash, looking for things, though I didn't know what. I looked for lines or sectors, the diamond shapes of daylight stars. Sometimes, silver-winged jets from the air force base across the hills turned the right way against the sun and went off like small flash bulbs on the horizon. There was nothing that struck me and stayed, though, nothing with the brilliance of white light or electric explosion that I thought came with discovery, so after a while I changed my idea of discovery. I just stood on the roof and stared. When my mother asked me, I told her that I might be seeing new things but that seeing change took time. "It's slow," I told her. "It may take years."

The first time I let her steal I chalked it up to surprise. I was working the front register when she walked in, a thin, tall woman in a plaid dress that looked wilted. She went right to the standup display of cut-price, nearly expired breads and crackers, where she took a loaf of rye from the shelf. Then she turned and looked me in the eye. We were looking into each other's eyes when she walked out the front door. Through the blue-and-white LOOK UP TO STAR FOOD sign on the window I watched her cross the street.

151

There were two or three other shoppers in the store, and over the tops of the potato chip packages I could see my mother's broom. My father was in back unloading chicken parts. Nobody else had seen her come in; nobody had seen her leave. I locked the cash drawer and walked to the aisle where my mother was sweeping.

"I think someone just stole."

My mother wheeled a trash receptacle when she swept, and as I stood there she closed it, put down her broom, and wiped her face with her handkerchief. "You couldn't get him?"

"It was a her."

"A lady?"

"I couldn't chase her. She came in and took a loaf of rye and left."

I had chased plenty of shoplifters before. They were kids usually, in sneakers and coats too warm for the weather. I chased them up the aisle and out the door, then to the corner and around it while ahead of me they tried to toss whatever it was—Twinkies, freeze-pops—into the sidewalk hedges. They cried when I caught them, begged me not to tell their parents. First time, my father said, scare them real good. Second time, call the law. I took them back with me to the store, held them by the collar as we walked. Then I sat them in the straight-back chair in the stockroom and gave them a speech my father had written. It was printed on a blue index card taped to the door. DO YOU KNOW WHAT YOU HAVE DONE? it began. DO YOU KNOW WHAT IT IS TO STEAL? I learned to pause between the questions, pace the room, check the card. "Give them time to get scared," my father said. He was expert at this. He never talked to them until he had dusted the vegetables or run a couple of women through the register. "Why should I stop my work for a kid who steals from me?"

he said. When he finally came into the stockroom he moved and spoke the way policemen do at the scene of an accident. His manner was slow and deliberate. First he asked me what they had stolen. If I had recovered whatever it was, he took it and held it up to the light, turned it over in his fingers as if it were of large value. Then he opened the freezer door and led the kid inside to talk about law and punishment amid the frozen beef carcasses. He paced as he spoke, breathed clouds of vapor into the air.

In the end, though, my mother usually got him to let them off. Once when he wouldn't, when he had called the police to pick up a third-offense boy who sat trembling in the stockroom, my mother called him to the front of the store to talk to a customer. In the stockroom we kept a key to the back door hidden under a silver samovar that belonged to my grandmother, and when my father was in front that afternoon my mother came to the rear, took it out, and opened the back door. She leaned down to the boy's ear. "Run," she said.

The next time she came in it happened the same way. My father was at the vegetable tier, stacking avocados. My mother was in back listening to the radio. It was afternoon. I rang in a customer, then looked up while I was putting the milk cartons in the bottom of the bag, and there she was. Her gray eyes were looking into mine. She had two cans of pineapple juice in her hands, and on the way out she held the door for an old woman.

That night I went up to clean the star. The air was clear. It was warm. When I finished wiping the glass I moved out over the edge of the eaves and looked into the distance where little turquoise squares—lighted swimming pools—stood out against the hills.

"Dade—"

It was my father's voice from behind the peak of the roof.

"Yes?"

"Come over to this side."

I mounted the shallow-pitched roof, went over the peak, and edged down the other slope to where I could see his silhouette against the lights on Route 5. He was smoking. I got up and we stood together at the edge of the shingled eaves. In front of us trucks rumbled by on the interstate, their trailers lit at the edges like the mast lights of ships.

"Look across the highway," he said.

"I am."

"What do you see?"

"Cars."

"What else?"

"Trucks."

For a while he didn't say anything. He dragged a few times on his cigarette, then pinched off the lit end and put the rest back in the pack. A couple of motorcycles went by, a car with one headlight, a bus.

"Do you know what it's like to live in a shack?" he said.

"No."

"You don't want to end up in a place like that. And it's damn easy to do if you don't know what you want. You know how easy it is?"

"Easy," I said.

"You have to know what you want."

For years my father had been trying to teach me competence and industry. Since I was nine I had been squeeze-drying mops before returning them to the closet, double-counting change, sweeping under the lip of the vegetable bins even if the dirt there was invisible to customers. On the basis of industry, my father said, Star Food had grown from a two-aisle, one-freezer corner store to the largest grocery in Arcade. When I was eight he had bought the failing gas station next door and built additions, so that now Star Food had nine aisles, separate coolers for dairy, soda, and beer, a tiered vegetable stand, a glass-fronted butcher counter, a part-time butcher, and, under what used to be the rain roof of the failing gas station, free parking while you shopped. When I started high school we moved into the apartment next door, and at meals we discussed store improvements. Soon my father invented a grid system for easy location of foods. He stayed up one night and painted, and the next morning there was a new coordinate system on the ceiling of the store. It was a grid, A through J, 1 through 10. For weeks there were drops of blue paint in his eyelashes.

A few days later my mother pasted up fluorescent stars among the grid squares. She knew about the real constellations and was accurate with the ones she stuck to the ceiling, even though she also knew that the aisle lights in Star Food stayed on day and night, so that her stars were going to be invisible. We saw them only once, in fact, in a blackout a few months later, when they lit up in hazy clusters around the store.

"Do you know why I did it?" she asked me the night of the blackout as we stood beneath their pale light.

"No."

"Because of the idea."

She was full of ideas, and one was that I was accomplishing something on the shallow-pitched section of our roof. Sometimes she sat at the dormer window and watched me. Through the glass I could see the slender outlines of her cheekbones. "What do you see?" she asked. On warm nights

155

she leaned over the sill and pointed out the constellations. "They are the illumination of great minds," she said.

After the woman walked out the second time I began to think a lot about what I wanted. I tried to discover what it was, and I had an idea it would come to me on the roof. In the evenings I sat up there and thought. I looked for signs. I threw pebbles down into the street and watched where they hit. I read the newspaper, and stories about ballplayers or jazz musicians began to catch my eye. When he was ten years old, Johnny Unitas strung a tire from a tree limb and spent afternoons throwing a football through it as it swung. Dizzy Gillespie played with an orchestra when he was seven. There was an emperor who ruled China at age eight. What could be said about me? He swept the dirt no one could see under the lip of the vegetable bins.

The day after the woman had walked out the second time, my mother came up on the roof while I was cleaning the star. She usually wore medium heels and stayed away from the shingled roof, but that night she came up. I had been over the glass once when I saw her coming through the dormer window, skirt hem and white shoes lit by moonlight. Most of the insects were cleaned off and steam was drifting up into the night. She came through the window, took off her shoes, and edged down the roof until she was standing next to me at the star. "It's a beautiful night," she said.

"Cool."

"Dade, when you're up here do you ever think about what is in the mind of a great man when he makes a discovery?"

The night was just making its transition from the thin sky to the thick, the air was taking on weight, and at the horizon distances were shortening. I looked out over the plain and tried to think of an answer. That day I had been thinking about a story my father occasionally told. Just before he and my mother were married he took her to the top of the hills that surround Arcade. They stood with the New Jerusalem River, western California, and the sea on their left, and Arcade on their right. My father has always planned things well, and that day as they stood in the hill pass a thunderstorm covered everything west, while Arcade, shielded by hills, was lit by the sun. He asked her which way she wanted to go. She must have realized it was a test, because she thought for a moment and then looked to the right, and when they drove down from the hills that day my father mentioned the idea of a grocery. Star Food didn't open for a year after, but that was its conception, I think, in my father's mind. That afternoon as they stood with the New Jerusalem flowing below them, the plains before them, and my mother in a cotton skirt she had made herself, I think my father must have seen right through to the end of his life.

I had been trying to see right through the end of my life, too, but these thoughts never led me in any direction. Sometimes I sat and remembered the unusual things that had happened to me. Once I had found the perfect, shed skin of a rattlesnake. My mother told my father that this indicated my potential for science. I was on the roof another time when it hailed apricot-size balls of ice on a summer afternoon. The day was hot and there was only one cloud, but as it approached from the distance it spread a shaft of darkness below it as if it had fallen through itself to the earth, and when it reached the New Jerusalem the river began throwing up spouts of water. Then it crossed onto land and I could see the hailstones denting parked cars. I went back inside the attic and watched it pass, and when I came outside again and picked up the ice balls that rolled between the corrugated roof spouts, their prickly edges melted in my fingers. In a minute they were gone. That was the rarest thing that ever happened to me. Now I waited for rare things because it seemed to me that if you traced back the lives of men you arrived at some sort of sign, rainstorm at one horizon and sunlight at the other. On the roof I waited for mine. Sometimes I thought about the woman and sometimes I looked for silhouettes in the blue shapes between the clouds.

"Your father thinks you should be thinking about the store," said my mother.

"I know."

"You'll own the store some day."

There was a carpet of cirrus clouds in the distance, and we watched them as their bottom edges were gradually lit by the rising moon. My mother tilted back her head and looked up into the stars. "What beautiful names," she said. "Cassiopeia, Lyra, Aquila."

"The Big Dipper," I said.

"Dade?"

"Yes?"

"I saw the lady come in yesterday."

"I didn't chase her."

"I know."

"What do you think of that?"

"I think you're doing more important things," she said. "Dreams are more important than rye bread." She took the bobby pins from her hair and held them in her palm. "Dade, tell me the truth. What do you think about when you come up here?"

In the distance there were car lights, trees, aluminum power poles. There were several ways I could have answered.

I said, "I think I'm about to make a discovery."

After that my mother began meeting me at the bottom of the stairs when I came down from the roof. She smiled expectantly. I snapped my fingers, tapped my feet. I blinked and looked at my canvas shoe-tips. She kept smiling. I didn't like this so I tried not coming down for entire afternoons, but this only made her look more expectant. On the roof my thoughts piled into one another. I couldn't even think of something that was undiscovered. I stood and thought about the woman.

Then my mother began leaving little snacks on the sill of the dormer window. Crackers, cut apples, apricots. She arranged them in fan shapes or twirls on a plate, and after a few days I started working regular hours again. I wore my smock and checked customers through the register and went upstairs only in the evenings. I came down after my mother had gone to sleep. I was afraid the woman was coming back, but I couldn't face my mother twice a day at the bottom of the stairs. So I worked and looked up at the door whenever customers entered. I did stock work when I could, stayed in back where the air was refrigerated, but I sweated anyway. I unloaded melons, tuna fish, cereal. I counted the cases of freeze-pops, priced the cans of All-American ham. At the swinging door between the stockroom and the back of the store my heart went dizzy. The woman knew something about me.

In the evenings on the roof I tried to think what it was. I saw mysterious new clouds, odd combinations of cirrus and stratus. How did she root me into the linoleum floor with her gray stare? Above me on the roof the sky was simmering. It was blue gas. I knew she was coming back.

It was raining when she did. The door opened and I felt the wet breeze, and when I looked up she was standing with her back to me in front of the shelves of cheese and dairy, and this time I came out from the counter and stopped behind her. She smelled of the rain outside.

"Look," I whispered, "why are you doing this to me?"

She didn't turn around. I moved closer. I was gathering my words, thinking of the blue index card, when the idea of limited fame came into my head. I stopped. How did human beings understand each other across huge spaces except with the lowest of ideas? I have never understood what it is about rain that smells, but as I stood there behind the woman I suddenly realized I was smelling the inside of clouds. What was between us at that moment was an idea we had created ourselves. When she left with a carton of milk in her hand I couldn't speak.

On the roof that evening I looked into the sky, out over the plains, along the uneven horizon. I thought of the view my father had seen when he was a young man. I wondered whether he had imagined Star Food then. The sun was setting. The blues and oranges were mixing into black, and in the distance windows were lighting up along the hillsides.

"Tell me what I want," I said then. I moved closer to the edge of the eaves and repeated it. I looked down over the alley, into the kitchens across the way, into living rooms, bedrooms, across slate rooftops. "Tell me what I want," I called. Cars pulled in and out of the parking lot. Big rigs rushed by on the interstate. The air around me was as cool as water, the lighted swimming pools like pieces of the daytime sky. An important moment seemed to be rushing up. "Tell me what I want," I said again.

Then I heard my father open the window and come out onto the roof. He walked down and stood next to me, the bald spot on top of his head reflecting the streetlight. He took out a cigarette, smoked it for a while, pinched off the end.

160

A bird fluttered around the light pole across the street. A car crossed below us with the words JUST MARRIED on the roof.

"Look," he said, "your mother's tried to make me understand this." He paused to put the unsmoked butt back in the pack. "And maybe I can. You think the gal's a little down and out; you don't want to kick her when she's down. OK, I can understand that. So I've decided something, and you want to know what?"

He shifted his hands in his pockets and took a few steps toward the edge of the roof.

"You want to know what?"

"What?"

"I'm taking you off the hook. Your mother says you've got a few thoughts, that maybe you're on the verge of something, so I decided it's OK if you let the lady go if she comes in again."

"What?"

"I said it's OK if you let the gal go. You don't have to chase her."

"You're going to let her steal?"

"No," he said. "I hired a guard."

He was there the next morning in clothes that were all dark blue. Pants, shirt, cap, socks. He was only two or three years older than I was. My father introduced him to me as Mr. Sellers. "Mr. Sellers," he said, "this is Dade." He had a badge on his chest and a ring of keys the size of a doughnut on his belt. At the door he sat jingling them.

I didn't say much to him, and when I did my father came out from the back and counted register receipts or stocked impulse items near where he sat. We weren't saying anything important, though. Mr. Sellers didn't carry a gun, only the doughnut-size key ring, so I asked him if he wished he did.

"Sure," he said.

"Would you use it?"

"If I had to."

I thought of him using his gun if he had to. His hands were thick and their backs were covered with hair. This seemed to go along with shooting somebody if he had to. My hands were thin and white and the hair on them was like the hair on a girl's cheek.

During the days he stayed by the front. He smiled at customers and held the door for them, and my father brought him sodas every hour or so. Whenever the guard smiled at a customer I thought of him trying to decide whether he was looking at the shoplifter.

And then one evening everything changed.

I was on the roof. The sun was low, throwing slanted light. From beyond the New Jerusalem and behind the hills, four air force jets appeared. They disappeared, then appeared again, silver dots trailing white tails. They climbed and cut and looped back, showing dark and light like a school of fish. When they turned against the sun their wings flashed. Between the hills and the river they dipped low onto the plain, then shot upward and toward me. One dipped, the others followed. Across the New Jerusalem they turned back and made two great circles, one inside the other, then dipped again and leveled off in my direction. The sky seemed small enough for them to fall through. I could see the double tails, then the wings and the jets. From across the river they shot straight toward the store, angling up so I could see the V-wings and camouflage and rounded bomb bays, and I covered my ears, and in a moment they were across the water and then they were above me, and as they passed over they barrel-rolled and flew upside down and showed me their black cockpit glass so that my heart came up into my mouth.

I stood there while they turned again behind me and lifted back toward the hills, trailing threads of vapor, and by the time their booms subsided I knew I wanted the woman to be caught. I had seen a sign. Suddenly the sky was water-clear. Distances moved in, houses stood out against the hills, and it seemed to me that I had turned a corner and now looked over a rain-washed street. The woman was a thief. This was a simple fact and it presented itself to me simply. I felt the world dictating its course.

I went downstairs and told my father I was ready to catch her. He looked at me, rolled the chewing gum in his cheek. "I'll be damned."

"My life is making sense," I said.

When I unloaded potato chips that night I laid the bags in the aluminum racks as if I were putting children to sleep in their beds. Dust had gathered under the lip of the vegetable bins, so I swept and mopped there and ran a wet cloth over the stalls. My father slapped me on the back a couple of times. In school once I had looked through a microscope at the tip of my own finger, and now as I looked around the store everything seemed to have been magnified in the same way. I saw cracks in the linoleum floor, speckles of color in the walls.

This kept up for a couple of days, and all the time I waited for the woman to come in. After a while it was more than just waiting; I looked forward to the day when she would return. In my eyes she would find nothing but resolve. How bright the store seemed to me then when I swept, how velvety the skins of the melons beneath the sprayer bottle. When I went up to the roof I scrubbed the star with the wet cloth and came back down. I didn't stare into the clouds and I didn't think about the woman except with the thought of catching her. I described her perfectly for the guard. Her gray eyes. Her plaid dress.

After I started working like this my mother began to go to the back room in the afternoons and listen to music. When I swept the rear I heard the melodies of operas. They came from behind the stockroom door while I waited for the woman to return, and when my mother came out she had a look about her of disappointment. Her skin was pale and smooth, as if the blood had run to deeper parts.

"Dade," she said one afternoon as I stacked tomatoes in a pyramid, "it's easy to lose your dreams."

"I'm just stacking tomatoes."

She went back to the register. I went back to stacking, and my father, who'd been patting me on the back, winking at me from behind the butcher counter, came over and helped me.

"I notice your mother's been talking to you."

"A little."

We finished the tomatoes and moved on to the lettuce.

"Look," he said, "it's better to do what you have to do, so I wouldn't spend your time worrying frontwards and backwards about everything. Your life's not so long as you think it's going to be."

We stood there rolling heads of butterball lettuce up the shallow incline of the display cart. Next to me he smelled like Aqua Velva.

"The lettuce is looking good," I said.

Then I went up to the front of the store. "I'm not sure what my dreams are," I said to my mother. "And I'm never going to discover anything. All I've ever done on the roof is look at the clouds."

Then the door opened and the woman came in. I was standing in front of the counter, hands in my pockets, my mother's eyes watering over, the guard looking out the window at a couple of girls, everything revolving around the point of calm that, in retrospect, precedes surprises. I'd been

164

waiting for her for a week, and now she came in. I realized I never expected her. She stood looking at me, and for a few moments I looked back. Then she realized what I was up to. She turned around to leave, and when her back was to me I stepped over and grabbed her.

I've never liked fishing much, even though I used to go with my father, because the moment a fish jumps on my line a tree's length away in the water I feel as if I've suddenly lost something. I'm always disappointed and sad, but now as I held the woman beneath the shoulder I felt none of this disappointment. I felt strong and good. She was thin, and I could make out the bones and tendons in her arm. As I led her back toward the stockroom, through the bread aisle, then the potato chips that were puffed and stacked like a row of pillows, I heard my mother begin to weep behind the register. Then my father came up behind me. I didn't turn around, but I knew he was there and I knew the deliberately calm way he was walking. "I'll be back as soon as I dust the melons," he said.

I held the woman tightly under her arm but despite this she moved in a light way, and suddenly, as we paused before the stockroom door, I felt as if I were leading her onto the dance floor. This flushed me with remorse. Don't spend your whole life looking backwards and forwards, I said to myself. Know what you want. I pushed the door open and we went in. The room was dark. It smelled of my whole life. I turned on the light and sat her down in the straight-back chair, then crossed the room and stood against the door. I had spoken to many children as they sat in this chair. I had frightened them, collected the candy they had tried to hide between the cushions, and presented it to my father when he came in. Now I looked at the blue card. DO YOU KNOW WHAT YOU HAVE DONE? it said. DO YOU KNOW WHAT IT IS TO STEAL?

I tried to think of what to say to the woman. She sat trembling slightly. I approached the chair and stood in front of her. She looked up at me. Her hair was gray around the roots.

"Do you want to go out the back?" I said.

She stood up and I took the key from under the silver samovar. My father would be there in a moment, so after I let her out I took my coat from the hook and followed. The evening was misty. She crossed the lot, and I hurried and came up next to her. We walked fast and stayed behind cars, and when we had gone a distance I turned and looked back. The stockroom door was closed. On the roof the star cast a pale light that whitened the aluminum-sided eaves.

It seemed we would be capable of a great communication now, but as we walked I realized I didn't know what to say to her. We went down the street without talking. The traffic was light, evening was approaching, and as we passed below some trees the streetlights suddenly came on. This moment has always amazed me. I knew the woman had seen it too, but it is always a disappointment to mention a thing like this. The streets and buildings took on their night shapes. Still we didn't say anything to each other. We kept walking beneath the pale violet of the lamps, and after a few more blocks I just stopped at one corner. She went on, crossed the street, and I lost sight of her.

I stood there until the world had rotated fully into the night, and for a while I tried to make myself aware of the spinning of the earth. Then I walked back toward the store. When they slept that night, my mother would dream of discovery and my father would dream of low-grade crooks. When I thought of this and the woman I was sad. It seemed you could never really know another person. I felt alone in the world, in the way that makes me aware of sound and temperature, as if I had just left a movie theater and stepped into an alley where a light rain was falling, and the wind was cool, and, from somewhere, other people's voices could be heard.

WINTER

Gary Paulsen

Wayne says there aren't any divisions in things. We had a big fight one time over whether or not there was a place between days when it wasn't the day before and it wasn't tomorrow yet. I said there were places, divisions in things so you could tell one from the next but he said no there wasn't and we set to it. By the time we were done I had a bloody nose and he had a swollen ear from where I hit him with a board and we still didn't know.

But there is a place where winter comes, a place to see it isn't fall any longer and know winter is here.

When the killing is done and the meat is up and the crops are in and the leaves have all gone to color and dropped off the trees and the gray limbs stick up like ugly fingers; when the barn is scraped clean inside and straw is laid for the first cold-weather bedding and the stock tank in back of the barn has ice on it that has to be broken in the mornings so the horses can drink; when you have to put choppers on your hands to fork hay down from the loft to the cows and the end of your nose gets cold and Rex moves into the barn to sleep and Father drains all the water out of all the radiators in the tractors and the old town truck and sometimes you suck a quick breath in the early morning that is so cold it makes your front teeth ache; when the chickens are walking around all fluffed up like white balls and the pigs burrow into the straw to sleep in the corner of their pen, and Mother goes to Hemings for the quilting bee they do each year that lasts a full day—when all that happens, fall is over.

But it still isn't winter.

When all the fall things are done there is the place between that Wayne says isn't so but is. There is something there and when we come out of the barn sometimes I can feel it. A sort of quiet. Once I stopped Wayne just as we were walking to the barn and it was getting dark and the clouds were sailing over our heads heading south and there was a north wind so you had to hold your head over into your collar to keep your ear warm; once then I stopped Wayne and asked him if he could feel it.

"Feel what?"

"Feel the place between," I said, and he looked at me and said he thought maybe I was crazy like those natives we read about in *National Geographic* who would predict weather and fall down.

But I didn't care and don't care now because I know the place is there. The place when fall is gone and winter hasn't come yet. It is a short time, in one night.

And then it snows.

First time.

You go to bed after chores and when you wake up and go downstairs and the sun starts to come up there is a new light to it, a brighter light; you look out the window and there is new snow all over everything.

169

First snow.

Soft and curved and white covering the yard and dirt and manure and grass and old leaves, the barns and granaries and machines out by the small tool shed, so that they don't look like buildings and machines at all but animals. White animals in the new light.

First snow.

Winter.

And winter isn't like any of the other parts of the year more than any other part isn't. Spring is close to summer, summer close to fall, but winter stands alone. That's how Uncle David says it. Back in the old country he said winter stood alone and now he says it stands alone here as well.

Winter comes in one night and of course Wayne and I look out the window in the morning and there are a million snow things to do.

After chores we take the grain shovels and slide down the river hill sitting on them, holding the handles up and trying to steer by pushing them. The first time they move kind of slow, but when the snow is packed they just fly down. We can't really steer them at all but just snort and whistle down the hill until we get so wet that Mother makes us come in and change.

Then we have to make snow forts and throw snowballs at each other. And the chickens. All fluffed and looking for a warm place to stand. If they come too close to the fort they get it, or Rex, or the cats, or anything.

. . . All the snow things to do. Father feels it too. One winter he hooked Stalker to a singletree with a rope out the back, and we stood on a piece of old tin roofing with a rope tied to it and we rode and rode, the tin so slick Stalker didn't know it was there. Big as he was the cold snapped him up and he acted like a colt, if colts can get as big as barns, just snorting and flipping his tail and making air, whipping that piece of tin and us all over the field in the snow until we were so cold and sopping that we were sticking to the tin.

Winter is all changes. Snow comes and makes it all different outside so things you see in the other times of the year are covered and gone. In back of the house there is an old elm that has a long sideways limb and one warm day some of the snow melted a bit and slipped down and then refroze so it looked like a picture of a snake we saw once in a magazine, or so Uncle David said. At night I could look out the bedroom window and see the snake hanging in the moonlight, the white snake and it seemed to move. It wasn't there in the summer or spring or fall but only in the winter. Like magic.

But finally, when the snow play is done and the barn and animals are settled in and the wood for the day finished, when our mittens are drying on the back of the kitchen stove and we have eaten the raw fried potatoes and strips of flank meat with the Watkins pepper on them and had the rhubarb sauce covered with separated cream, sitting at the kitchen table with the lantern hissing over our heads, finally when our stomachs are full Father pushes his chair away from the table and thanks Mother and God for the food and moves into the winter room. The living room.

Wayne and I have to do the dishes, and that includes washing the separator, which takes a long time, so when we get into the winter room the fire in the stove has been freshened with white oak and Mother is sitting knitting socks and mittens, and Father sits on one side of the stove and Uncle David sits on the other, with Nels next to him.

While Father has been filling the stove Mother has lighted the kerosene lamp so there is a soft yellow glow in the room. Wayne and I sit on the rug that Mother sewed out of braided rags, the colors all wrapped together in the soft light so they seem to move.

Father is working on his carving. I don't know when he started it. Maybe before I was born. But for as long as Wayne and I can remember he has been working at it every night in the winter. It will be a carving of a team of horses and a sleigh and trace chains and harnesses and reins and a man driving with a full load of pulp logs on the sleigh—all carved out of one piece of sugar-white pine he cut from a clear log many years ago. All we can see is the two horses' heads sticking out and part of one front shoulder, but Father can tell us where each thing is, pointing to where the links of chain will be and the logs and the man's head, just like he can see them even when they aren't there.

He carves quietly, his face even and somehow gentle, looking down as the small knife he uses cuts into the soft pine to peel away shavings so clear they look like honey in the yellow light from the lamp.

Wayne and I watch the fire in the stove through the mica windows in the door—all little squares—and the stove is like a friend. In the summer it is black and large and fills the corner of the room but now it is warm and part of us somehow. It is tall and narrow, and on top there is a silver ornament that looks like a big rose upside down. Around the side there is a silver rail that Wayne says is to put your feet on to warm them. But one night when nobody was looking I sneaked a spit on the rail and it snapped and sizzled like I'd spit on the top of the stove where it gets red, so I'm not about to stick a foot on that rail.

Next to the stove, across from Father, sits Uncle David and right next to him sits Nels. The two old men have straight-backed wooden chairs and a couple of old coffee cans they use

172

for spitting into. They both fill their lower lip with snoose*
after we eat, and they sit straight up in the chairs, and Nels
doesn't say anything except to slap his leg now and again
when a story gets good.

Every night in the winter it starts the same. Uncle David
and Nels will fill their lower lips and Father will carve and
Mother will knit and the yellow flames will make our faces
burn, and then Uncle David will spit in the coffee can and
rub his hands on his legs and take a breath and say:

"It was when I was young . . ."

Then he will tell the story of Alida who was his wife in the
old country. Always it is the same. Always he tells the story of
Alida first and it is the same story.

ALIDA

"It was when I was young and was thought fit only to sharpen
the tools of the older men. This was wrong, wrong then and
wrong now, but that is the way they did things in the old
country. So each day I sat in front of the cottage and drew
the stone over the axes and filed the saws until there was only
new steel and the axes could shave the hair off your arm.

"It was when I was young and a day came when a girl
walked by as I was sharpening tools and she was so beautiful
she made my tongue stick to the roof of my mouth and I
could not speak. Yellow hair she had, yellow hair like cornsilk
mixed with sunlight. It was so long she had it coiled in a braid
at the back of her head. And her eyes were clear blue. Ice blue.

---

* **snoose.** Finely ground tobacco.

173

She was carrying a towel filled with loaves of bread to take to
the cutters in the woods and she stopped and said good day to
me and I could not answer.

"Could not answer.

"And that was Alida. She became my wife and let her hair
down for me in great coils in the light from tallow candles. I
could not live without her. We were married there in the old
country and I put the handkerchief on my head to show I
would be a good husband. I grew from sharpening tools to
using an ax and a bucksaw and we planned to come to America, planned and saved. But soon Alida was with child and we
had to stay and when the child came it was a wrong birth and
the child died and Alida died and I died.

"I wandered into the woods along Nulsek Fjord, walked
in the snow and wind and would not have come back except
that my brother Nels came for me and found me and brought
me with him to America to work where there was new wood
to cut and woods that go to the sky. But I never remarried
and never looked at another woman and my heart has never
healed, and that is the story of Alida."

Uncle David always starts with the story of Alida. He has told
it so often that when it comes out there aren't many stops
except that his voice always hitches when he talks about Alida
letting her hair down in the light from the tallow candles and
I can see her so plain, so plain, and Mother always cries.

Father makes a small cough like there was something in
his throat and Wayne takes a deep breath and Nels looks at
the floor and doesn't move and Mother always cries and it is
quiet—so quiet when he finishes the story of Alida that it
seems as if time has stopped and we are all back with her and
the bread in towels and Uncle David sharpening the tools of
the older men.

Then Uncle David sighs and rubs his hands on his trouser leg and leans over to spit in the can and starts the second story of the night. The other stories are all different, always different night after night through the winter, so many stories I can't know them all or say them all.

But three of them I know.

Three of the stories make cuts across all the stories the way a bucksaw cuts across wood so you can see all the rings and know how old the tree is, so you can know all about the tree.

Three are the stories like rings and show how it was that Wayne, and maybe me a little, came close to ruining it all, killing it all.

So Uncle David sits and he spits in the can and rubs his legs with hands callused so thick they look like bone or wood and he sighs and starts each one the same.

ORUD THE TERRIBLE

"It was when I was young that Siggurd came to me and told me the story of Orud and the house under the sea.

"The story was from old times, when men went off in long boats and many did not come back and those who did had blood on their bodies and blood on their swords and blood in their hearts.

"Men took then, and did not give so much but took what they wanted. The man who took the most was Orud. Orud was tall and wide in the shoulder and had a helmet made of steel hammered to a point but soaked in salt until it was red, red like blood. They called him Orud the Red when they went a-viking and he was so terrible that it was said even the men in his boat feared him, and these men feared nothing.

175

"So it came that on one voyage they went to far shores where they had not been before. They found small houses along the shore which were not rich in gold but all had much in livestock and wool and flax and wheat, and Orud and his men went among them and took and took and killed and killed until their arms were tired with it and they had to stop.

"Orud had never taken a wife. But on this voyage in one of the houses along the sea his men found a woman of beauty and her name was Melena. Orud decided to claim her for a wife, which was his right as he was captain of the boat.

"But such was Melena's beauty, with long, red-gold hair to match the color of burnished steel and a straight back and long arms, such was her beauty that the man who found her wanted her as his own wife and claimed her, and that was his right as well.

"But Orud would not have Melena go to another man. So they fought and the other man was weaker, as all men were weaker than Orud, and the other man lost and was slain. Orud put his head on an oar to boast and would not even bury the man as his station demanded. It was an awful thing then, to kill one of your own men and not even give him a Viking funeral, but they set sail with good wind to head home. Orud tied Melena in the bow of the longboat so she could not escape.

"But she was more than beautiful. Melena was smart and strong, and she waited until the boat was entering the fjord of Orud's home village and they could hear the horns sounding, waited until all could see the boat and see her. Then she stood on the side and used her magic to release her bonds and threw herself into the water rather than be wed to Orud.

"Such was Orud's rage when she leaped that he forgot himself and jumped after her, to bring her back.

"But he forgot he was wearing armor and his sword and

helmet to be welcomed with his new wife. The weight took him down into the deeps and he was not seen again.

"Except that much bad came to the village. The people had sickness and their crops died and when they tried to go a-viking to make up for it their boats sank again and again.

"It was said that Orud had found Melena and taken her to be his wife though she did not want it, and that they lived in a cottage under the sea at the mouth of the fjord but that Melena had not forgiven the village for sending the boat which carried Orud to take her. It was said she cursed the village into sickness and waste and when she looked up and saw the village send out a boat she would spread her hair up from the bottom in long strands and catch the boat and sink it in vengeance and laugh at Orud, and the wind and waves were her laughter, and that is the story of Orud and Melena and the house beneath the sea."

The night of that story we sat quietly and thought of the cottage under the water and Melena's hair streaming up to gather in the boats, and Orud's terrible rage. Then Uncle David sighed and spit again and held his hands to the stove for the warmth. Mother shook her head thinking of the horror of Orud, and Nels coughed, and Uncle David gave a little chuckle and told the story of Crazy Alen.

CRAZY ALEN

"It was when I was still young but I had come to the new country and I was cutting in the woods.

"We were cutting in a camp called Folter, on the line between two counties then. I had a way with a file so they paid me extra to sharpen the saws at night and at times during the day. Because of that I was in camp many times when the other men were out cutting and so I knew more of the story of Crazy Alen than many of them.

"Alen came years before I did, came on a boat from the old country just as I did but long ago when they had to sail. He wasn't crazy at first but cut wood better than many men and was fast. He used a bucksaw and would pull so hard he often pulled the man on the other end off his feet, and the sawdust would fly out in a plume.

"But a day came when he started to play jokes on the other men in the camp. They were not bad jokes, didn't hurt anybody, and many laughed at them and that made him do all the more. He would put pepper in their snoose or sew their stockings closed or nail a board over the hole in the outhouse.

"He was finally known for his humor and the jokes became larger until one day he waited until the foreman—he disliked the foreman then—was in the outhouse and Alen dropped a Norway pine so big you couldn't reach around it, dropped it right in front of the door so close the foreman couldn't get out. It was the best of all his jokes, dropping the tree that close to the door, and took great skill. Trees don't always drop where they are supposed to drop. Everybody thought it very funny.

"Everybody except the foreman, who saw only the danger in it. Had the tree dropped a little to the side it would have crushed the whole outhouse with the foreman inside it.

"And so it came that the foreman fired Alen—they called him Crazy Alen by this time, because of his jokes—but Alen didn't mind. He was getting old by then and had decided to stop work and watch things for a while. He made himself a small cabin on the side of a narrow trail back in the forest.

"In the way these things work Alen and the foreman then became good friends. Part of it was that the foreman was also old and most of the rest of the crew was young; and part of it was that the foreman missed Alen's jokes and humor. He could not hire Alen back to work, because somebody might be hurt, but the foreman began to like Alen's jokes himself and one day he walked into the cabin with some honey in a bucket he'd stolen from the camp cook and a checkerboard.

"Soon he was walking back along the narrow trail once a week to play checkers and drink tea with honey and this went on through part of a winter, a spring, a summer and fall and into winter again. The two men would sit and drink tea and play checkers and speak of things they'd done when they were young, and not so young, in that small cabin in the forest.

"Of course Alen's jokes hadn't stopped. Every time the foreman came to play checkers Alen would have a new one, a bigger joke. He would have a bucket of water over the door with a trip lever set to drop when the foreman came in. Or he would loosen the rungs in the foreman's chair so it would collapse when he sat down. Or he would put salt in his tea. Since all of these jokes were aimed at the foreman you'd think he would get mad but things were different then, different and maybe a little rough, and so men didn't mind rough jokes and the foreman didn't mind Alen.

"Nobody can know how long it would have gone on, but that winter Alen felt death coming and decided to play his best joke of all. As a young man he had been big, big and heavy. Alen stood six-and-a-half feet and weighed two hundred and seventy pounds at least in his prime and his arms were long and heavy as well. He had come in and down with age, but the frame was still there and it was a big frame.

"In the middle of that winter when it was so cold you could spit and it would bounce, when steel ax heads broke if they weren't warmed before you chopped, in that cold Alen saw his death coming.

179

"Nobody knew how he could have done it, but just before he died he opened the cabin door to let the cold in and lay down on the floor on his back with his arms and legs stretched out as wide open as he could get them. And then he died.

"He died with a wide smile on his lips and his arms and legs out and his eyes staring wide open at the ceiling.

"And it was in the middle of the week and four days passed before the foreman came to play checkers. Four days with the door open Alen lay and the cold came into the room and the cold came into Alen and froze him as hard as granite. Then the foreman came and found him spread and solid on the floor.

"Alen knew these things. He knew the cabin had a small door and that the trail down through the woods was narrow and winding and he knew the foreman. He knew the foreman wouldn't be able to bring himself to break Alen's arms and legs and he knew the foreman would not dare to thaw Alen because of what would get soft with the thaw.

"He knew these things, Alen did, and he knew one more thing, knew the foreman would not leave the body. Could not leave the body.

"And so it was his greatest joke on the foreman because Alen would not fit through the door. The foreman had to use an ax to cut the door opening wider and then try to get Alen—spread and hard and smiling—get Alen down the trail. It was nearly impossible. He tried to carry Alen but he was too heavy. He tried to drag him. Finally he tried to roll him, cartwheel him, and where tree limbs were too low he used an ax to chop a way through.

"Two days and a night it took him to get Alen's body back to the camp. Two days wheeling and dragging and carrying the spread-eagled man and when he finally got to camp they put Alen in the back of a sleigh and it took two more days to get him to town and an undertaker. It was said that as the sleigh went down the road all those who saw Alen thought he was waving and they would laugh and wave back.

"And that is the story of Crazy Alen."

We sat then and listened, and Mother took a breath because she had been holding it, with one hand over her mouth, and I thought of death. Death never seemed funny to me. All I knew of it was when I had been sick and thought I would die and was afraid, or in the fall when we killed and killed. But it was impossible to think of Crazy Alen without smiling and that meant I was smiling at death, laughing at death and the picture of Alen with his arms and legs out and the foreman trying to get him down the trail.

There were many questions I wanted to ask and I knew Wayne wanted to ask some as well but we didn't. We never did. The stories were just there, not something to be questioned and opened up. Uncle David just told them and they came from him and went into us and became part of us so that his memory became our memory. But nothing about them was ever questioned.

Until he told the story that broke things.

It is strange, the way it happened, strange and kind of inside-out. It all came down to how Wayne felt about the stories. I always thought of them as just stories and didn't think they were real. I mean I know there probably aren't a man and woman living in a cottage under the sea—probably. Once Mother said the stories were not for believing so much as to be believed in.

But it was different for Wayne. I didn't know it, but it was different. Somehow the stories had mixed in his mind so they had become a real part of his thinking, so that he believed them. And even when he knew they couldn't be—knew there couldn't be a man and woman living in a cottage under the sea—even then he wanted them to be real, wanted her hair to take the ships down, and by wanting them to be real somehow they became real in his mind. And that's how the trouble started.

There is nothing I could have done about it anyway but if I could have stopped it, stopped the hurt I saw in Uncle David's eyes, I would have given anything.

We had spent a long day splitting and carrying stove wood in because the wind had come around to the northwest and it was picking up into a storm. Father said it would blow for three or four days and drop to forty below when it stopped snowing and blowing and we wanted to be ready for it. Father split with the big double-bladed ax he kept in the ax bin in the granary, each ax so sharp you could shave the hair on your arms with it, just as Uncle David said. Wayne and I weren't allowed to use them, not even to split kindling. They were axes that used to belong to Uncle David and to Nels when they cut wood in the old days and they were something to see. All shining and silver, the two blades on each honed with a small, circular stone. I had seen Uncle David and Nels sharpening them with the stones, sitting with peaceful smiles on their faces while the stone went round and round and I thought it was the same look Mother had sometimes when she was knitting. But I had never seen Uncle David or Nels use the axes and I figured it was because they were so old now that they couldn't use them because it would hurt them somehow.

So Father split wood and I asked to help carry it and Father said yes. I felt like I must have brought in most of a cord by myself, stacking it under the overhang on the porch. When we were done, finally, I couldn't see over the pile. It covered the whole porch and I thought there was enough for two weeks before Father finally put the ax away and we went to milk and do evening chores.

That night it was my turn to crank the separator and change the buckets, and by the time we at last went to the house for supper it was so dark the lantern light from the kitchen window made all the snow in the yard seem to glow. I was so tired my brain felt filled with rags.

Mother had made a big pile of mashed potatoes with meat gravy and I made a little lake of gravy in the middle and ate around the edges until I couldn't eat any more, and then, after Wayne and I did the dishes, we went into the living room.

Father started to carve and showed us how far he'd come along since last time and Mother nodded and smiled and Nels and Uncle David filled their lower lips and talked about how the snow cover was good for the crops next year. Then they talked about work that needed doing, and I was watching the fire through the small window on the stove door and my eyes closed and I was sleeping. Or half sleeping. Just going in and out of it when I heard Uncle David start a story—and it wasn't about Alida.

THE WOODCUTTER

"It was when I was young but I was old enough to have come to the new country and to the north woods and was working as a cutter.

"In the first winter we cut in the lake country and used the lakes and rivers as ice roads for the teams and sleighs.

Boys too young to cut took water sleighs with tanks of water in them and soaked the grooves where the runners ran to keep them slick, and put hay in the downhill grooves to slow the loads so they wouldn't run over the teams. I tell you we moved some wood and those horses got so strong they could haul a load as big as a house down to the rivers where the logs were left on the ice to float down the rivers to the sawmills in the spring floods.

"I don't even know how much wood we cut. One camp didn't speak with another, one company didn't speak with another. We just cut and cut until there wasn't anything left. Where there had been forest so thick you couldn't see ten yards without looking at a giant Norway or white pine, you could stand on level ground and see fifteen miles and nothing higher than a stump when we were done cutting.

"It was sad and most of us wished we hadn't done it when it was finished but it was that way then just as it is now that the forest has started to grow up some again. People just cut without thinking.

"But this isn't a story about the cutting so much as it is about a man who was young then.

"There were many men who were good cutters because that was a time when all men were cutters, and there are stories about most of them. Some could use a saw this way and some could use an ax that way. There were stories of men who could cut a six-inch pine with a single swing of a double-bitted ax and other men who shaved with axes and still others who could make saws and axes sing and weep and bleed. But there was one man who they said could do all these things.

"It was said that no man could use an ax like him. The wood of the handle seemed to grow out of his hands and there was nothing he could not do. Men in the camps would stop work to watch him and this becomes important when you know that men were paid by how much they cut. To stop meant they did not receive pay.

"But he was such a wonder with an ax that they would stop. The young man would walk to a tree and swing and the chips would float off like they were made of air—chopping half the head and more deep with each blow so the tree would almost fly off the stump when he cut through.

"They said many things of him. They said he could put a match in a stump so the head was sticking up and swing the ax with his eyes closed and catch the match perfectly so that it would split and both sides would light.

"And it was true.

"They said he shaved each day with an ax and never cut himself and his cheek was as smooth as a baby's.

"And it was true.

"They said he could take a four-foot piece of cordwood and swing two axes, one in each hand, swing them into the two ends and the wood would split clean and the axes would meet in the middle.

"And it was true. . . ."

Here Father caught his breath and looked up sharply and said across the stove:

"But that was you. All those things were about you. . . ."

And I felt Wayne stiffen next to me on the rug. I turned to look at him and saw he was staring at Uncle David so hard he seemed to stare a hole through him. Wayne was mad. No, more than mad, tight with it, tight with mad the way he got when Philly Hansen took him down again and again in front of the girls at school.

Hurt mad.

185

Mad like to burn with it—Wayne was raw mad and I could tell he wanted to say something but he didn't because we never talked during the stories.

Uncle David coughed a little and spit in the can and looked for a long time at Father and then finished the story. It was about how the young man who was the best cutter of all thought that his new life would last forever only it didn't. None of it lasted. The woods were gone and he was old, and it ended that way but I didn't hear much of it because Wayne kept staring at Uncle David. He kept stiff like wood and staring at him and I knew something was wrong but I couldn't understand what it could be.

And when the stories were done that night and we went up to our room and got under the quilts to hide from the cold, even then I didn't learn because Wayne just turned away and didn't say anything. I knew he was awake because his breathing was tight and ragged somehow. I wanted to talk to him about whatever it was but he said nothing. I tried to stay awake but the whole day of wood and work and cranking the separator and listening to the stories and the heat from the stove and the cold from the bedroom and the warmth from the stacked quilts on top came crashing down on me and I fell asleep almost before my eyes closed.

In the morning we went outside for morning chores and Wayne looked a little funny at Uncle David in the barn but he didn't seem so mad anymore and I thought whatever it was had passed.

But I was wrong, so wrong, and I would see a thing so awful I wished I had never seen it. . . .

Wayne and I have a special place in the granary in back of the oats bin. I guess it isn't very much of a place but it's close and cozy and sometimes we sit there and talk about things. It wasn't something we planned so much as it just happened when we were small and as we got older we just would find ourselves there now and again when we wanted to talk. That day Wayne looked at me and walked toward the granary. I knew he wanted to talk so I followed. It was just after chores and barely light so I left the door open because there wasn't a lantern in the granary and it was pitch dark. Even with the light coming in the door it was still pretty gray.

"He's lying," Wayne said, as soon as I came in. He was sitting on an overturned bucket by the door so I went in and squatted in the corner.

"Who's lying?"

"Uncle David. All the time he's been lying with the stories, just telling us lies."

"But they're only stories. They aren't real. They're supposed to be lies. . . ."

"It's that he put himself up as one of the heroes—a great thing. That makes it all bragging and not just stories. Bragging makes it all a lie on a lie. How could anyone cut a match in half blindfolded? How could anyone make two axes meet in the center of a log? That's just all lies. It's all lies and he's a liar and a braggart.

"Don't you see? Father caught him at it. Uncle David told lies about himself and that makes it all lies, just lies and lies and lies."

I was surprised to see that Wayne was crying, that it hurt him, this thing of Uncle David and the stories. He was crying and he said over and over:

"Liar, liar, liar . . ."

And that would have been bad enough but I looked up, over Wayne and there was Uncle David and I knew he had heard most of it, maybe all of it, because his eyes were full of pain; they looked like the pig's eyes just after Father cut its throat and it knew it was going to die. All pain and confused, all fall killing pain and confused Uncle David's eyes were, so hurt and ripped that it seemed he would crumble, and I could not shut Wayne up.

"Lies, all lies, and he's a liar, a liar, a liar . . ."

I tried to make a sign, to show Wayne, but it was too late. Uncle David turned slowly and seemed to cave in and walked away and then I told Wayne, finally I got it out, and Wayne felt bad but not as bad as I thought he should.

It was over, and Uncle David was broken and done.

That night we ate supper and it was good but tasted like wood in my mouth. I saw Wayne who usually ate like a granary dog just pick and pick at his potatoes.

After supper we went into the living room and Uncle David didn't tell a story.

Not even the story of Alida.

He sat and rubbed his face and Father talked and Mother talked and even Nels talked but there was no story, none of anything like a story. Just talk of chores and summer crops and Mother spoke a little of the neighbors who were having trouble with a sick baby, and I thought it was like fall and something had been killed.

Here, I thought, in this room a thing has died. I nearly cried and wished Wayne would be hurt for what he'd done.

And another night

And another night.

Nothing like a story—just talk and talk until we went up to bed. I started to hate Wayne then and think he should be punished—and on the fourth or fifth day after he broke Uncle David we were in the hayloft.

Many times we went into the hayloft to fool around. It was fun to swing on the trip rope that carried the hay up into the barn when we stored it. We would swing from the little landing up under the roof near the top of the loft down on the trip rope and land in the soft hay. It was something I never got tired of because the hay would catch you, just let you sink soft and down, and it smelled nice.

But this time I was still mad at Wayne, mad and sick of him so it went bad. I made a swing and landed on his leg and he squealed a bit and before I could stop it I was on top of him beating him and crying and cursing him for what he'd done to Uncle David.

We fought around the loft and down the side of the hay, only of course he's bigger than me so it wasn't much of a fight. Pretty soon he was sitting on top of me and he gave me a clout that made my nose bleed.

I got madder then and went a little crazy but he still held me down and clamped my arms to my side while I just squirmed and I was trying to bite him when I looked up and he wasn't paying any attention.

The way we had fallen we were jammed back into the corner where the logs were crossed in together. Because the barn was very old, some of the logs had warped so there were small gaps between them. Father said if it had been a house he would have chinked it and filled the holes, but it being a barn they just ventilated the hay nice and kept it dry—like a big crib.

Wayne was looking at something through the cracks in the corner and when I saw how interested he was I forgot all about fighting.

He let me loose and I pulled up alongside of him and wiped blood off my lip and nose and looked out the crack and saw Uncle David.

In the back of the barn was a large pile of wood cut in four-foot lengths for shipment to the paper mills. Father and some other men in the neighborhood cut the wood each fall and haul it out to the railroad when the roads get frozen and slick enough for the bobsleds, and it brings in a little extra money for Christmas.

Uncle David was standing staring at the pile of wood. His arms hung down at his sides and he looked small and sad somehow and I hated Wayne again for what he'd done. I thought it would be right for me to go down to him and touch him, maybe on the hand, and lean against his leg the way I did sometimes but before I could move Uncle David turned away from the stack of wood and walked to the granary.

I thought it was over, that time when I could have touched him, but in a few seconds he came out of the granary.

He was carrying two axes. He had one in each hand, two double-bitted axes, big and shiny and sharp as razors and I knew then, I knew what he had planned and I thought no, no. I must have moved because Wayne put a hand on my arm and held a finger to his lips.

"Be still. . . ."

"But he'll hurt himself," I whispered.

Wayne didn't answer. He'd turned away and was looking out through the cracks again and I did too. I couldn't stop.

I couldn't stop though I didn't want to see it, the way I couldn't stop when they killed the pigs and chickens in the fall—I couldn't stop looking through the cracks.

Back at the woodpile Uncle David took a log down, studied it, pushed it aside and took another one. The logs looked heavy and big, bigger than him. He seemed so caved in and tiny, and when he finally got the log in the right place on the ground he had to stop and catch his breath and I thought no, no, no I should run for Mother or Father and have them stop him because he should not do this and it will hurt him.

But now it was too late and I knew that, too, knew that it would be terrible to keep him from at least trying.

He stood to the side of the log facing it and held the axhandles, one on each side with the heads of the axes resting on the ground and all of him was curved down onto the axes so they looked like hickory crutches. He was a broken and tired and sad old man, and there wasn't a thing he could do, I thought, even to lift the axes: So awful a thing, the way he stood, the axes standing at his side, his hands on the handles and little bits of steam coming from his breath as he looked down at the log and I thought no.

Please no. And no matter what it would do, no matter if Wayne tried to stop me, I was going to run down and tell him that he didn't have to do this, that it didn't matter.

But now he moved his head up and looked at the sky and the sun caught his face and we could see it plain, see his face in the sun. The wrinkles seemed to leave. The skin seemed to smooth as the sun covered his face.

And his hands tightened on the axhandles and the heads of the axes in the snow, the heads trembled a little and it was as if something came from the earth.

Some thing, some power passed from the earth up through the silver axheads and through the hickory handles and it started in his arms. A little movement, then the arms seemed to swell and his shoulders came up and filled and his back straightened and his whole body filled with it until he was standing straight and tall and I heard Wayne's breath come in and stop and mine did the same.

"He's young again," Wayne whispered and it was not just a whisper but more a worshiping thing, like part of a prayer, and he was right.

Uncle David stood before the log and he was young, and as we watched, as we could not turn away and we watched, the axes started to move.

Up.

They came up from the snow. The heavy axheads came up and out to the side, came up like they were floating on light air, up and up until they were over his head, one on each side, the sun catching them and splashing the silver from the heads down on him like a new light, a life light and they hung there for what seemed like hours, days, hung in the air over his head while we held our breath. And just when it seemed that all things had stopped, that nothing would or could ever happen again, just then they started down.

Down.

So slowly at first the silver heads began to swing down and then faster and faster until they were two silver curves of light, two streaks curving down and around Uncle David so fast they were just a blur coming into the ends of the log.

Thunnnnkkk!

Such a clean sound. The silver curves went into the log clean and even and the log opened and split and the axes met exactly in the middle with a small metal sound.

"Oh . . ." Wayne whispered but he did not know he'd said it.

"Oh."

For a second, a long second, Uncle David stood there, the axes touching in front of him and I was crying and Wayne was crying.

"We have to go down there," I said. "We have to go down there and tell him we saw it."

But Wayne held my arm and shook his head and said, "No. It was for him. All for him. Don't you see? If we go down there it will ruin it for him."

And of course he was right because Wayne is sometimes right, and I settled back down into the hay and looked out the crack again.

Uncle David stood tall for part of another second, then the power all went out of him. His shoulders and back curved down again and his arms seemed to settle on the axhandles and he became old, old and bent. He carefully laid the axes on the ground and bent for the log. He put the two split halves back up in the stack, turned so nobody would see them. Then he picked up the axes and carried them to the granary and put them away and came out, spit in the snow once and walked to the house, bent and old and tired and down.

We watched him through the crack all that time. Watched him walk until he was gone inside the house, the two of us crying, and that night when chores were done and we'd eaten a big supper we went into the living room and Uncle David told us about Alida. Then he told a tale about a man who lived in the forest who was so ugly he couldn't be seen and he sent messages of love to a girl on the wing feathers of birds and Wayne listened and I listened and I knew we would listen for always.

HIGH SCHOOL GRADUATION

Maya Angelou

The children in Stamps* trembled visibly with anticipation. Some adults were excited too, but to be certain the whole young population had come down with graduation epidemic. Large classes were graduating from both the grammar school and the high school. Even those who were years removed from their own day of glorious release were anxious to help with preparations as a kind of dry run. The junior students who were moving into the vacating classes' chairs were tradition-bound to show their talents for leadership and management. They strutted through the school and around the campus exerting pressure on the lower grades. Their authority was so new that occasionally if they pressed a little too hard it had to be overlooked. After all, next term was coming, and it never hurt a sixth grader to have a play sister in the eighth grade, or a tenth-year student to be able to call

---

* The town in Arkansas where the author lived.

194

a twelfth grader Bubba. So all was endured in a spirit of shared understanding. But the graduating classes themselves were the nobility. Like travelers with exotic destinations on their minds, the graduates were remarkably forgetful. They came to school without their books, or tablets, or even pencils. Volunteers fell over themselves to secure replacements for the missing equipment. When accepted, the willing workers might or might not be thanked, and it was of no importance to the pregraduation rites. Even teachers were respectful of the now quiet and aging seniors, and tended to speak to them, if not as equals, as beings only slightly lower than themselves. After tests were returned and grades given, the student body, which acted like an extended family, knew who did well, who excelled, and what piteous ones had failed.

Unlike the white high school, Lafayette County Training School distinguished itself by having neither lawn, nor hedges, nor tennis court, nor climbing ivy. Its two buildings (main classrooms, the grade school and home economics) were set on a dirt hill with no fence to limit either its boundaries or those of bordering farms. There was a large expanse to the left of the school which was used alternately as a baseball diamond or basketball court. Rusty hoops on swaying poles represented the permanent recreational equipment, although bats and balls could be borrowed from the P. E. teacher if the borrower was qualified and if the diamond wasn't occupied.

Over this rocky area relieved by a few shady tall persimmon trees the graduating class walked. The girls often held hands and no longer bothered to speak to the lower students. There was a sadness about them, as if this old world was not their home and they were bound for higher ground. The boys, on the other hand, had become more friendly, more outgoing. A decided change from the closed attitude they projected while studying for finals. Now they seemed not ready to give up the old school, the familiar paths and classrooms. Only a small percentage would be continuing on to college—one of the South's A & M (agricultural and mechanical) schools, which trained Negro youths to be carpenters, farmers, handymen, masons, maids, cooks, and baby nurses. Their future rode heavily on their shoulders, and blinded them to the collective joy that had pervaded the lives of the boys and girls in the grammar school graduating class.

Parents who could afford it had ordered new shoes and ready-made clothes for themselves from Sears and Roebuck or Montgomery Ward. They also engaged the best seam-stresses to make the floating graduating dresses and to cut down secondhand pants which would be pressed to a military slickness for the important event.

Oh, it was important, all right. Whitefolks would attend the ceremony, and two or three would speak of God and home, and the Southern way of life, and Mrs. Parsons, the principal's wife, would play the graduation march while the lower-grade graduates paraded down the aisles and took their seats below the platform. The high school seniors would wait in empty classrooms to make their dramatic entrance.

In the Store* I was the person of the moment. The birth-day girl. The center. Bailey† had graduated the year before, although to do so he had had to forfeit all pleasures to make up for his time lost in Baton Rouge.

My class was wearing butter-yellow piqué dresses, and Momma launched out on mine. She smocked the yoke into

---

* The store owned by the author's family.

† The author's brother.

tiny crisscrossing puckers, then shirred the rest of the bodice. Her dark fingers ducked in and out of the lemony cloth as she embroidered raised daisies around the hem. Before she considered herself finished she had added a crocheted cuff on the puff sleeves, and a pointy crocheted collar.

I was going to be lovely. A walking model of all the various styles of fine hand sewing and it didn't worry me that I was only twelve years old and merely graduating from the eighth grade. Besides, many teachers in Arkansas Negro schools had only that diploma and were licensed to impart wisdom.

The days had become longer and more noticeable. The faded beige of former times had been replaced with strong and sure colors. I began to see my classmates' clothes, their skin tones, and the dust that waved off pussy willows. Clouds that lazed across the sky were objects of great concern to me. Their shiftier shapes might have held a message that in my new happiness and with a little bit of time I'd soon decipher. During that period I looked at the arch of heaven so religiously my neck kept a steady ache. I had taken to smiling more often, and my jaws hurt from the unaccustomed activity. Between the two physical sore spots, I suppose I could have been uncomfortable, but that was not the case. As a member of the winning team (the graduating class of 1940) I had outdistanced unpleasant sensations by miles. I was headed for the freedom of open fields.

Youth and social approval allied themselves with me and we trammeled memories of slights and insults. The wind of our swift passage remodeled my features. Lost tears were pounded to mud and then to dust. Years of withdrawal were brushed aside and left behind, as hanging ropes of parasitic moss.

My work alone had awarded me a top place and I was going to be one of the first called in the graduating ceremonies. On the classroom blackboard, as well as on the bulletin board in the auditorium, there were blue stars and white stars and red stars. No absences, no tardinesses, and my academic work was among the best of the year. I could say the preamble to the Constitution even faster than Bailey. We timed ourselves often: "WethepeopleoftheUnitedStates inordertoformamoreperfectunion . . ." I had memorized the Presidents of the United States from Washington to Roosevelt in chronological as well as alphabetical order.

My hair pleased me too. Gradually the black mass had lengthened and thickened, so that it kept at last to its braided pattern, and I didn't have to yank my scalp off when I tried to comb it.

Louise and I had rehearsed the exercises until we tired out ourselves. Henry Reed was class valedictorian. He was a small, very black boy with hooded eyes, a long, broad nose, and an oddly shaped head. I had admired him for years because each term he and I vied for the best grades in our class. Most often he bested me, but instead of being disappointed I was pleased that we shared top places between us. Like many Southern Black children, he lived with his grandmother, who was as strict as Momma and as kind as she knew how to be. He was courteous, respectful, and soft-spoken to elders, but on the playground he chose to play the roughest games. I admired him. Anyone, I reckoned, sufficiently afraid or sufficiently dull could be polite. But to be able to operate at a top level with both adults and children was admirable.

His valedictory speech was entitled "To Be or Not to Be." The rigid tenth-grade teacher had helped him write it. He'd been working on the dramatic stresses for months.

The weeks until graduation were filled with heady activities. A group of small children were to be presented in a play about buttercups and daisies and bunny rabbits. They could be heard throughout the building practicing their hops and their little songs that sounded like silver bells. The older girls (nongraduates, of course) were assigned the task of making refreshments for the night's festivities. A tangy scent of ginger, cinnamon, nutmeg, and chocolate wafted around the home economics building as the budding cooks made samples for themselves and their teachers.

In every corner of the workshop, axes and saws split fresh timber as the woodshop boys made sets and stage scenery. Only the graduates were left out of the general bustle. We were free to sit in the library at the back of the building or look in quite detachedly, naturally, on the measures being taken for our event.

Even the minister preached on graduation the Sunday before. His subject was, "Let your light so shine that men will see your good works and praise your Father, Who is in Heaven." Although the sermon was purported to be addressed to us, he used the occasion to speak to backsliders, gamblers, and general ne'er-do-wells. But since he had called our names at the beginning of the service we were mollified.

Among Negroes the tradition was to give presents to children going only from one grade to another. How much more important this was when the person was graduating at the top of the class. Uncle Willie and Momma had sent away for a Mickey Mouse watch like Bailey's. Louise gave me four embroidered handkerchiefs. (I gave her crocheted doilies.) Mrs. Sneed, the minister's wife, made me an undershirt to wear for graduation, and nearly every customer gave me a nickel or maybe even a dime with the instruction "Keep on moving to higher ground," or some such encouragement.

Amazingly the great day finally dawned and I was out of bed before I knew it. I threw open the back door to see it more clearly, but Momma said, "Sister, come away from that door and put your robe on."

I hoped the memory of that morning would never leave me. Sunlight was itself young, and the day had none of the insistence maturity would bring it in a few hours. In my robe and barefoot in the backyard, under cover of going to see about my new beans, I gave myself up to the gentle warmth and thanked God that no matter what evil I had done in my life He had allowed me to live to see this day. Somewhere in my fatalism I had expected to die, accidentally, and never have the chance to walk up the stairs in the auditorium and gracefully receive my hard-earned diploma. Out of God's merciful bosom I had won reprieve.

Bailey came out in his robe and gave me a box wrapped in Christmas paper. He said he had saved his money for months to pay for it. It felt like a box of chocolates, but I knew Bailey wouldn't save money to buy candy when we had all we could want under our noses.

He was as proud of the gift as I. It was a soft-leather-bound copy of a collection of poems by Edgar Allan Poe, or, as Bailey and I called him, "Eap." I turned to "Annabel Lee" and we walked up and down the garden rows, the cool dirt between our toes, reciting the beautifully sad lines.

Momma made a Sunday breakfast although it was only Friday. After we finished the blessing, I opened my eyes to find the watch on my plate. It was a dream of a day. Everything went smoothly and to my credit. I didn't have to be reminded or scolded for anything. Near evening I was too jittery to attend to chores, so Bailey volunteered to do all before his bath.

Days before, we had made a sign for the Store, and as we turned out the lights Momma hung the cardboard over the doorknob. It read clearly: CLOSED. GRADUATION.

My dress fitted perfectly and everyone said that I looked like a sunbeam in it. On the hill, going toward the school,

Bailey walked behind with Uncle Willie, who muttered, "Go on, Ju." He wanted him to walk ahead with us because it embarrassed him to have to walk so slowly. Bailey said he'd let the ladies walk together, and the men would bring up the rear. We all laughed, nicely.

Little children dashed by out of the dark like fireflies. Their crepe-paper dresses and butterfly wings were not made for running and we heard more than one rip, dryly, and the regretful "uh uh" that followed.

The school blazed without gaiety. The windows seemed cold and unfriendly from the lower hill. A sense of ill-fated timing crept over me, and if Momma hadn't reached for my hand I would have drifted back to Bailey and Uncle Willie, and possibly beyond. She made a few slow jokes about my feet getting cold, and tugged me along to the now-strange building.

Around the front steps, assurance came back. There were my fellow "greats," the graduating class. Hair brushed back, legs oiled, new dresses and pressed pleats, fresh pocket handkerchiefs and little handbags, all homesewn. Oh, we were up to snuff, all right. I joined my comrades and didn't even see my family go in to find seats in the crowded auditorium.

The school band struck up a march and all classes filed in as had been rehearsed. We stood in front of our seats, as assigned, and on a signal from the choir director, we sat. No sooner had this been accomplished than the band started to play the national anthem. We rose again and sang the song, after which we recited the pledge of allegiance. We remained standing for a brief minute before the choir director and the principal signaled to us, rather desperately I thought, to take our seats. The command was so unusual that our carefully rehearsed and smooth-running machine was thrown off. For a full minute we fumbled for our chairs and bumped into each

201

other awkwardly. Habits change or solidify under pressure, so in our state of nervous tension we had been ready to follow our usual assembly pattern: the American national anthem, then the pledge of allegiance, then the song every Black person I knew called the Negro National Anthem.* All done in the same key, with the same passion and most often standing on the same foot.

Finding my seat at last, I was overcome with a presentiment of worse things to come. Something unrehearsed, unplanned, was going to happen, and we were going to be made to look bad. I distinctly remember being explicit in the choice of pronoun. It was "we," the graduating class, the unit, that concerned me then.

The principal welcomed "parents and friends" and asked the Baptist minister to lead us in prayer. His invocation was brief and punchy, and for a second I thought we were getting on the high road to right action. When the principal came back to the dais, however, his voice had changed. Sounds always affected me profoundly and the principal's voice was one of my favorites. During assembly it melted and lowed weakly into the audience. It had not been in my plan to listen to him, but my curiosity was piqued and I straightened up to give him my attention.

He was talking about Booker T. Washington, our "late great leader," who said we can be as close as the fingers on the hand, etc. . . . Then he said a few vague things about friendship and the friendship of kindly people to those less fortunate than themselves. With that his voice nearly faded, thin, away. Like a river diminishing to a stream and then to a trickle. But he cleared his throat and said, "Our speaker

---

* "Lift Ev'ry Voice and Sing."

tonight, who is also our friend, came from Texarkana to deliver the commencement address, but due to the irregularity of the train schedule, he's going to, as they say, 'speak and run.' " He said that we understood and wanted the man to know that we were most grateful for the time he was able to give us and then something about how we were willing always to adjust to another's program, and without more ado—"I give you Mr. Edward Donleavy."

Not one but two white men came through the door offstage. The shorter one walked to the speaker's platform, and the tall one moved to the center seat and sat down. But that was our principal's seat, and already occupied. The dislodged gentleman bounced around for a long breath or two before the Baptist minister gave him his chair; then with more dignity than the situation deserved, the minister walked off the stage.

Donleavy looked at the audience once (on reflection, I'm sure that he wanted only to reassure himself that we were really there), adjusted his glasses, and began to read from a sheaf of papers.

He was glad "to be here and to see the work going on just as it was in the other schools."

At the first "Amen" from the audience I willed the offender to immediate death by choking on the word. But Amens and Yes, sir's began to fall around the room like rain through a ragged umbrella.

He told us of the wonderful changes we children in Stamps had in store. The Central School (naturally, the white school was Central) had already been granted improvements that would be in use in the fall. A well-known artist was coming from Little Rock to teach art to them. They were going to have the newest microscopes and chemistry equipment for their laboratory. Mr. Donleavy didn't leave us long in the dark over who made these improvements available to Central High. Nor were we to be ignored in the general betterment scheme he had in mind.

He said that he had pointed out to people at a very high level that one of the first-line football tacklers at Arkansas Agricultural and Mechanical College had graduated from good old Lafayette County Training School. Here fewer Amens were heard. Those few that did break through lay dully in the air with the heaviness of habit.

He went on to praise us. He went on to say how he had bragged that "one of the best basketball players at Fisk sank his first ball right here at Lafayette County Training School."

The white kids were going to have a chance to become Galileos and Madame Curies and Edisons and Gauguins, and our boys (the girls weren't even in on it) would try to be Jesse Owenses and Joe Louises.

Owens and the Brown Bomber were great heroes in our world, but what school official in the white-goddom of Little Rock had the right to decide that those two men must be our only heroes? Who decided that for Henry Reed to become a scientist he had to work like George Washington Carver, as a bootblack, to buy a lousy microscope? Bailey was obviously always going to be too small to be an athlete, so which concrete angel glued to what country seat had decided that if my brother wanted to become a lawyer he had to first pay penance for his skin by picking cotton and hoeing corn and studying correspondence books at night for twenty years?

The man's dead words fell like bricks around the auditorium and too many settled in my belly. Constrained by hard-learned manners I couldn't look behind me, but to my left and right the proud graduating class of 1940 had dropped their heads. Every girl in my row had found something new to do with her handkerchief. Some folded the tiny squares into love knots, some into triangles, but most were wadding them, then pressing them flat on their yellow laps.

On the dais, the ancient tragedy was being replayed. Professor Parsons sat, a sculptor's reject, rigid. His large, heavy body seemed devoid of will or willingness, and his eyes said he was no longer with us. The other teachers examined the flag (which was draped stage right) or their notes, or the windows which opened on our now-famous playing diamond.

Graduation, the hush-hush magic time of frills and gifts and congratulations and diplomas, was finished for me before my name was called. The accomplishment was nothing. The meticulous maps, drawn in three colors of ink, learning and spelling decasyllabic words, memorizing the whole of *The Rape of Lucrece*—it was for nothing. Donleavy had exposed us.

We were maids and farmers, handymen and washerwomen, and anything higher that we aspired to was farcical and presumptuous.

Then I wished that Gabriel Prosser and Nat Turner had killed all whitefolks in their beds and that Abraham Lincoln had been assassinated before the signing of the Emancipation Proclamation, and that Harriet Tubman had been killed by that blow on her head and Christopher Columbus had drowned in the *Santa Maria*.

It was awful to be a Negro and have no control over my life. It was brutal to be young and already trained to sit quietly and listen to charges brought against my color with no chance of defense. We should all be dead. I thought I should like to see us all dead, one on top of the other. A pyramid of flesh with the whitefolks on the bottom, as the broad base, then the Indians with their silly tomahawks and teepees and wigwams and treaties, the Negroes with their mops and recipes and cotton sacks and spirituals sticking out of their mouths. The

Dutch children should all stumble in their wooden shoes and break their necks. The French should choke to death on the Louisiana Purchase (1803) while silkworms ate all the Chinese with their stupid pigtails. As a species, we were an abomination. All of us.

Donleavy was running for election, and assured our parents that if he won we could count on having the only colored paved playing field in that part of Arkansas. Also—he never looked up to acknowledge the grunts of acceptance—also, we were bound to get some new equipment for the home economics building and the workshop.

He finished, and since there was no need to give any more than the most perfunctory thank-you's, he nodded to the men on the stage, and the tall white man who was never introduced joined him at the door. They left with the attitude that now they were off to something really important. (The graduation ceremonies at Lafayette County Training School had been a mere preliminary.)

The ugliness they left was palpable. An uninvited guest who wouldn't leave. The choir was summoned and sang a modern arrangement of "Onward, Christian Soldiers," with new words pertaining to graduates seeking their place in the world. But it didn't work. Elouise, the daughter of the Baptist minister, recited "Invictus," and I could have cried at the impertinence of "I am the master of my fate, I am the captain of my soul."

My name had lost its ring of familiarity and I had to be nudged to go and receive my diploma. All my preparations had fled. I neither marched up to the stage like a conquering Amazon, nor did I look in the audience for Bailey's nod of approval. Marguerite Johnson, I heard the name again, my honors were read, there were noises in the audience of appreciation, and I took my place on the stage as rehearsed.

I thought about colors I hated: ecru, puce, lavender, beige, and black.

There was shuffling and rustling around me, then Henry Reed was giving his valedictory address, "To Be or Not to Be." Hadn't he heard the whitefolks? We couldn't *be,* so the question was a waste of time. Henry's voice came out clear and strong. I feared to look at him. Hadn't he got the message? There was no "nobler in the mind" for Negroes because the world didn't think we had minds, and they let us know it. "Outrageous fortune"? Now, that was a joke. When the ceremony was over I had to tell Henry Reed some things. That is, if I still cared. Not "rub," Henry, "erase." "Ah, there's the erase." Us.

Henry had been a good student in elocution. His voice rose on tides of promise and fell on waves of warnings. The English teacher had helped him to create a sermon winging through Hamlet's soliloquy. To be a man, a doer, a builder, a leader, or to be a tool, an unfunny joke, a crusher of funky toadstools. I marveled that Henry could go through with the speech as if we had a choice.

I had been listening and silently rebutting each sentence with my eyes closed; then there was a hush, which in an audience warns that something unplanned is happening. I looked up and saw Henry Reed, the conservative, the proper, the A student, turn his back to the audience and turn to us (the proud graduating class of 1940) and sing, nearly speaking,

"Lift ev'ry voice and sing
 Till earth and heaven ring
 Ring with the harmonies of Liberty . . ."

It was the poem written by James Weldon Johnson. It was the music composed by J. Rosamond Johnson. It was the Negro national anthem. Out of habit we were singing it.

Our mothers and fathers stood in the dark hall and joined the hymn of encouragement. A kindergarten teacher led the small children onto the stage and the buttercups and daisies and bunny rabbits marked time and tried to follow:

"Stony the road we trod
   Bitter the chastening rod
   Felt in the days when hope, unborn, had died.
   Yet with a steady beat
   Have not our weary feet
   Come to the place for which our fathers sighed?"

Each child I knew had learned that song with his ABC's and along with "Jesus Loves Me This I Know." But I personally had never heard it before. Never heard the words, despite the thousands of times I had sung them. Never thought they had anything to do with me.

On the other hand, the words of Patrick Henry had made such an impression on me that I had been able to stretch myself tall and trembling and say, "I know not what course others may take, but as for me, give me liberty or give me death."

And now I heard, really for the first time:

"We have come over a way that with tears
      has been watered,
   We have come, treading our path through
      the blood of the slaughtered."

While echoes of the song shivered in the air, Henry Reed bowed his head, said "Thank you," and returned to his place in the line. The tears that slipped down many faces were not wiped away in shame.

We were on top again. As always, again. We survived. The depths had been icy and dark, but now a bright sun spoke to our souls. I was no longer simply a member of the proud graduating class of 1940; I was a proud member of the wonderful, beautiful Negro race.

Oh, Black known and unknown poets, how often have your auctioned pains sustained us? Who will compute the lonely nights made less lonely by your songs, or the empty pots made less tragic by your tales?

If we were a people much given to revealing secrets, we might raise monuments and sacrifice to the memories of our poets, but slavery cured us of that weakness. It may be enough, however, to have it said that we survive in exact relationship to the dedication of our poets (include preachers, musicians, and blues singers).

Adventures of Huckleberry Finn

Mark Twain

CHAPTER 7

I FOOL PAP AND GET AWAY

"Git up! What you 'bout?"

I opened my eyes and looked around, trying to make out where I was. It was after sun-up, and I had been sound asleep. Pap was standing over me looking sour—and sick, too. He says:

"What you doin' with this gun?"

I judged he didn't know nothing about what he had been doing, so I says:

"Somebody tried to get in, so I was laying for him."

"Why didn't you roust me out?"

"Well, I tried to but I couldn't; I couldn't budge you."

"Well, all right. Don't stand there palavering all day, but out with you and see if there's a fish on the lines for breakfast. I'll be along in a minute."

He unlocked the door and I cleared out up the riverbank. I noticed some pieces of limbs and such things floating down, and a sprinkling of bark; so I knowed the river had begun to rise. I reckoned I would have great times now if I was over at the town. The June rise used to be always luck for me, because as soon as that rise begins here comes cordwood floating down, and pieces of log rafts—sometimes a dozen logs together, so all you have to do is catch them and sell them to the woodyards and the sawmill.

I went along up the bank with one eye out for pap and t'other one out for what the rise might fetch along. Well, all at once here comes a canoe; just a beauty, too, about thirteen or fourteen foot long, riding high like a duck. I shot head-first off of the bank like a frog, clothes and all on, and struck out for the canoe. I just expected there'd be somebody laying down in it, because people often done that to fool folks, and when a chap had pulled a skiff out most to it they'd raise up and laugh at him. But it warn't so this time. It was a drift-canoe sure enough, and I clumb in and paddled her ashore. Thinks I, the old man will be glad when he sees this—she's worth ten dollars. But when I got to shore pap wasn't in sight yet, and as I was running her into a little creek like a gully, all hung over with vines and willows, I struck another idea: I judged I'd hide her good and then, 'stead of taking to the woods when I run off, I'd go down the river about fifty mile and camp in one place for good and not have such a rough time tramping on foot.

It was pretty close to the shanty and I thought I heard the old man coming all the time, but I got her hid, and then I out and looked around a bunch of willows and there was the old man down the path a piece just drawing a bead on a bird with his gun. So he hadn't seen anything.

When he got along I was hard at it taking up a trot-line. He abused me a little for being so slow, but I told him I fell in the river and that was what made me so long. I knowed he would see I was wet, and then he would be asking questions. We got five catfish off the lines and went home.

While we laid off after breakfast to sleep up, both of us being about wore out, I got to thinking that if I could fix up some way to keep pap and the widow from trying to follow me, it would be a certainer thing than trusting to luck to get far enough off before they missed me; you see, all kinds of things might happen. Well, I didn't see no way for a while but by and by pap raised up a minute to drink another barrel of water, and he says:

"Another time a man comes a-prowling round here you roust me out, you hear? That man warn't here for no good. I'd 'a' shot him. Next time you roust me out, you hear?"

Then he dropped down and went to sleep again; what he had been saying give me the very idea I wanted. I says to myself, I can fix it now so nobody won't think of following me.

About twelve o'clock we turned out and went along up the bank. The river was coming up pretty fast, and lots of driftwood going by on the rise. By and by along comes part of a log raft—nine logs fast together. We went out with the skiff and towed it ashore. Then we had dinner. Anybody but pap would 'a' waited and seen the day through, so as to catch more stuff, but that warn't pap's style. Nine logs was enough for one time; he must shove right over to town and sell. So he locked me in and took the skiff and started off towing the raft about half past three. I judged he wouldn't come back that night. I waited till I reckoned he had got a good start, then I out with my saw and went to work on that log again. Before he was t'other side of the river I was out of the hole; him and his raft was just a speck on the water away off yonder.

I took the sack of corn meal and took it to where the canoe was hid and shoved the vines and branches apart and put it in; then I done the same with the side of bacon, then the whisky-jug. I took all the coffee and sugar there was and all the ammunition; I took the wadding; I took the bucket and gourd; took a dipper and a tin cup and my old saw and two blankets and the skillet and the coffee-pot. I took fish-lines and matches and other things—everything that was worth a cent. I cleaned out the place. I wanted an ax but there wasn't any, only the one out at the woodpile, and I knowed why I was going to leave that. I fetched out the gun and now I was done.

I had wore the ground a good deal crawling out of the hole and dragging out so many things. So I fixed that as good as I could from the outside by scattering dust on the place, which covered up the smoothness and the sawdust. Then I fixed the piece of log back into its place and put two rocks under it and one against it to hold it there, for it was bent up at that place and didn't quite touch ground. If you stood four or five foot away and didn't know it was sawed, you wouldn't never notice it; and besides, this was the back of the cabin and it warn't likely anybody would go fooling around there.

It was all grass clear to the canoe, so I hadn't left a track. I followed around to see. I stood on the bank and looked out over the river. All safe. So I took the gun and went up a piece into the woods and was hunting around for some birds when I see a wild pig; hogs soon went wild in them bottoms after they had got away from the prairie farms. I shot this fellow and took him into camp.

I took the ax and smashed in the door. I beat it and hacked it considerable a-doing it. I fetched the pig in and took him back nearly to the table and hacked into his throat with the ax and laid him down on the ground to bleed; I say ground because it *was* ground—hard packed and no boards. Well, next I took an old sack and put a lot of big rocks in it— all I could drag—and I started it from the pig and dragged it to the door and through the woods down to the river and dumped it in, and down it sunk, out of sight. You could easy see that something had been dragged over the ground. I did wish Tom Sawyer was there; I knowed he would take an interest in this kind of business and throw in the fancy touches. Nobody could spread himself like Tom Sawyer in such a thing as that.

Well, last I pulled out some of my hair and blooded the ax good, and stuck it on the back side and slung the ax in the corner. Then I took up the pig and held him to my breast with my jacket (so he couldn't drip) till I got a good piece below the house and then dumped him into the river. Now I thought of something else. So I went and got the bag of meal and my old saw out of the canoe and fetched them to the house. I took the bag to where it used to stand and ripped a hole in the bottom of it with the saw, for there warn't no knives and forks on the place—pap done everything with his clasp-knife about the cooking. Then I carried the sack about a hundred yards across the grass and through the willows east of the house, to a shallow lake that was five mile wide and full of rushes—and ducks too, you might say, in the season. There was a slough or a creek leading out of it on the other side that went miles away, I don't know where, but it didn't go to the river. The meal sifted out and made a little track all the way to the lake. I dropped pap's whetstone there too, so as to look like it had been done by accident. Then I tied up the rip in the meal-sack with a string, so it wouldn't leak no more, and took it and my saw to the canoe again.

It was about dark now; so I dropped the canoe down the river under some willows that hung over the bank and waited for the moon to rise. I made fast to a willow; then I took a bite to eat and by and by laid down in the canoe to smoke a pipe and lay out a plan. I says to myself, they'll follow the track of that sackful of rocks to the shore and then drag the river for me. And they'll follow that meal track to the lake and go browsing down the creek that leads out of it to find the robbers that killed me and took the things. They won't ever hunt the river for anything but my dead carcass. They'll soon get tired of that and won't bother no more about me. All right; I can stop anywhere I want to. Jackson's Island is good enough for me; I know that island pretty well and nobody ever comes there. And then I can paddle over to town, nights, and slink around and pick up things I want. Jackson's Island's the place.

I was pretty tired and the first thing I knowed I was asleep. When I woke up I didn't know where I was for a minute. I set up and looked around, a little scared. Then I remembered. The river looked miles and miles across. The moon was so bright I could 'a' counted the drift-logs that went a-slipping along, black and still, hundreds of yards out from shore. Everything was dead quiet, and it looked late and *smelt* late. You know what I mean—I don't know the words to put it in.

I took a good gap and a stretch, and was just going to unhitch and start when I heard a sound away over the water. I listened. Pretty soon I made it out. It was that dull kind of a regular sound that comes from oars working in rowlocks when it's a still night. I peeped out through the willow branches, and there it was—a skiff, away across the water. I couldn't tell how many was in it. It kept a-coming, and when it was abreast of me I see there warn't but one man in it. Thinks I, maybe it's pap, though I warn't expecting him. He dropped below me with the current, and by and by he come a-swinging up shore in the easy water, and he went by so close

215

I could 'a' reached out the gun and touched him. Well, it *was* pap, sure enough—and sober, too, by the way he laid to his oars.

I didn't lose no time. The next minute I was a-spinning downstream, soft but quick, in the shade of the bank. I made two mile and a half and then struck out a quarter of a mile or more towards the middle of the river, because pretty soon I would be passing the ferry-landing and people might see me and hail me. I got out amongst the driftwood and then laid down in the bottom of the canoe and let her float. I laid there and had a good rest and a smoke out of my pipe, looking away into the sky; not a cloud in it. The sky looks ever so deep when you lay down on your back in the moonshine; I never knowed it before. And how far a body can hear on the water such nights! I heard people talking at the ferry-landing. I heard what they said, too—every word of it. One man said it was getting towards the long days and the short nights now. T'other one said *this* warn't one of the short ones, he reckoned—and then they laughed, and he said it over again and they laughed again; then they waked up another fellow and told him and laughed; but he didn't laugh, he ripped out something brisk and said let him alone. The first fellow said he 'lowed to tell it to his old woman—she would think it was pretty good; but he said that warn't nothing to some things he had said in his time. I heard one man say it was nearly three o'clock and he hoped daylight wouldn't wait more than about a week longer. After that the talk got further and further away and I couldn't make out the words anymore, but I could hear the mumble and now and then a laugh, too, but it seemed a long ways off.

I was away below the ferry now. I rose up, and there was Jackson's Island, about two mile and a half downstream, heavy-timbered and standing up out of the middle of the river, big and dark and solid, like a steamboat without any lights. There warn't any signs of the bar at the head—it was all under water now.

It didn't take me long to get there. I shot past the head at a ripping rate, the current was so swift, and then I got into the dead water and landed on the side towards the Illinois shore. I run the canoe into a deep dent in the bank that I knowed about; I had to part the willow branches to get in, and when I made fast nobody could 'a' seen the canoe from the outside.

I went up and set down on a log at the head of the island and looked out on the big river and the black driftwood and away over to the town, three mile away, where there was three or four lights twinkling. A monstrous big lumber-raft was about a mile upstream, coming along down, with a lantern in the middle of it. I watched it come creeping down, and when it was most abreast of where I stood I heard a man say, "Stern oars, there! heave her head to stabboard!" I heard that just as plain as if the man was by my side.

There was a little gray in the sky now; so I stepped into the woods, and laid down for a nap before breakfast.

CHAPTER 8

I SPARE MISS WATSON'S JIM

The sun was up so high when I waked that I judged it was after eight o'clock. I laid there in the grass and the cool shade, thinking about things and feeling rested and ruther comfortable and satisfied. I could see the sun out at one or two holes, but mostly it was big trees all about, and gloomy in there amongst them. There was freckled places on the ground where the light sifted down through the leaves, and the freckled places swapped about a little, showing there was a little breeze up there. A couple of squirrels set on a limb and jabbered at me very friendly.

I was powerful lazy and comfortable—didn't want to get up and cook breakfast. Well, I was dozing off again when I thinks I hears a deep sound of "boom!" away up the river. I rouses up and rests on my elbow and listens; pretty soon I hears it again. I hopped, and went and looked out at a hole in the leaves, and I see a bunch of smoke laying on the water a long ways up—about abreast the ferry. And there was the ferryboat full of people floating along down. I knowed what was the matter now. "Boom!" I see the white smoke squirt out of the ferryboat's side. You see, they was firing cannon over the water, trying to make my carcass come to the top.

I was pretty hungry but it warn't going to do for me to start a fire, because they might see the smoke. So I set there and watched the cannon-smoke and listened to the boom. The river was a mile wide there and it always looks pretty on a summer morning—so I was having a good enough time seeing them hunt for my remainders if I only had a bite to eat. Well, then I happened to think how they always put quicksilver in loaves of bread and float them off, because they always go right to the drownded carcass and stop there. So, says I, I'll keep a lookout and if any of them's floating around after me I'll give them a show. I changed to the Illinois edge of the island to see what luck I could have, and I warn't disappointed. A big double loaf come along and I most got it with a long stick, but my foot slipped and she floated out further. Of course I was where the current set in the closest to the shore—I knowed enough for that. But by and by along comes another one and this time I won. I took out the plug and shook out the little dab of quicksilver, and set my teeth in. It was "baker's bread"—what the quality eat, none of your lowdown corn-pone.

I got a good place amongst the leaves and set there on a log, munching the bread and watching the ferryboat and very well satisfied. And then something struck me. I says, now I reckon the widow or the parson or somebody prayed that this bread would find me, and here it has gone and done it. So there ain't no doubt but there is something in that thing— that is, there's something in it when a body like the widow or the parson prays but it don't work for me, and I reckon it don't work for only just the right kind.

I lit a pipe and had a good long smoke and went on watching. The ferryboat was floating with the current and I allowed I'd have a chance to see who was aboard when she come along, because she would come in close, where the bread did. When she'd got pretty well along down towards me, I put out my pipe and went to where I fished out the bread and laid down behind a log on the bank in a little open place. Where the log forked I could peep through.

By and by she come along, and she drifted in so close that they could 'a' run out a plank and walked ashore. Most everybody was on the boat. Pap, and Judge Thatcher, and Bessie Thatcher, and Joe Harper, and Tom Sawyer, and his old Aunt Polly, and Sid and Mary, and plenty more. Everybody was talking about the murder but the captain broke in and says:

"Look sharp, now; the current sets in the closest here and maybe he's washed ashore and got tangled amongst the brush at the water's edge. I hope so, anyway."

I didn't hope so. They all crowded up and leaned over the rails, nearly in my face, and kept still, watching with all their might. I could see them first-rate but they couldn't see me. Then the captain sung out, "Stand away!" and the cannon let off such a blast right before me that it made me deef with the

noise and pretty near blind with the smoke, and I judged I
was gone. If they'd 'a' had some bullets in, I reckon they'd 'a'
got the corpse they was after. Well, I see I warn't hurt, thanks
to goodness. The boat floated on and went out of sight
around the shoulder of the island. I could hear the booming
now and then, further and further off, and by and by, after
an hour, I didn't hear it no more. The island was three mile
long. I judged they had got to the foot and was giving it up.
But they didn't yet awhile. They turned around the foot of
the island and started up the channel on the Missouri side,
under steam, and booming once in a while as they went. I
crossed over to that side and watched them. When they got
abreast the head of the island they quit shooting and dropped
over to the Missouri shore and went home to the town.

I knowed I was all right now. Nobody else would come
a-hunting after me. I got my traps out of the canoe and
made me a nice camp in the thick woods. I made a kind of a
tent out of my blankets to put my things under so the rain
couldn't get at them. I catched a catfish and haggled him
open with my saw, and towards sundown I started my campfire and had supper. Then I set out a line to catch some fish
for breakfast.

When it was dark I set by my campfire smoking and feeling
pretty satisfied, but by and by it got sort of lonesome, and so I
went and set on the bank and listened to the current swashing
along and counted the stars and drift-logs and rafts that come
down and then went to bed; there ain't no better way to put
in time when you are lonesome; you can't stay so, you soon
get over it.

And so for three days and nights. No difference—just the
same thing. But the next day I went exploring around down
through the island. I was boss of it; it all belonged to me,
so to say, and I wanted to know all about it, but mainly I

wanted to put in the time. I found plenty strawberries, ripe and prime, and green summer grapes and green razberries; and the green blackberries was just beginning to show. They would all come handy by and by, I judged.

Well, I went fooling along in the deep woods till I judged I warn't far from the foot of the island. I had my gun along but I hadn't shot nothing, it was for protection; thought I would kill some game nigh home. About this time I mighty near stepped on a good-sized snake and it went sliding off through the grass and flowers, and I after it, trying to get a shot at it. I clipped along, and all of a sudden I bounded right onto the ashes of a campfire that was still smoking.

My heart jumped up amongst my lungs. I never waited for to look further, but uncocked my gun and went sneaking back on my tiptoes as fast as ever I could. Every now and then I stopped a second amongst the thick leaves and listened, but my breath come so hard I couldn't hear nothing else. I slunk along another piece further, then listened again, and so on and so on. If I see a stump, I took it for a man; if I trod on a stick and broke it, it made me feel like a person had cut one of my breaths in two and I only got half, and the short half, too.

When I got to camp I warn't feeling very brash, there warn't much sand in my craw, but I says, this ain't no time to be fooling around. So I got all my traps into my canoe again so as to have them out of sight, and I put out the fire and scattered the ashes around to look like an old last-year's camp, and then clumb a tree.

I reckon I was up in the tree two hours, but I didn't see nothing, I didn't hear nothing—I only *thought* I heard and seen as much as a thousand things. Well, I couldn't stay up there forever; so at last I got down, but I kept in the thick woods and on the lookout all the time. All I could get to eat was berries and what was left over from breakfast.

By the time it was night I was pretty hungry. So when it was good and dark I slid out from shore before moonrise and paddled over to the Illinois bank—about a quarter of a mile. I went out in the woods and cooked a supper, and I had about made up my mind I would stay there all night when I hear a *plunkety-plunk, plunkety-plunk,* and says to myself, horses coming, and next I hear people's voices. I got everything into the canoe as quick as I could, and then went creeping through the woods to see what I could find out. I hadn't got far when I hear a man say:

"We better camp here if we can find a good place; the horses is about beat out. Let's look around."

I didn't wait but shoved out and paddled away easy. I tied up in the old place, and reckoned I would sleep in the canoe.

I didn't sleep much. I couldn't, somehow, for thinking. And every time I waked up I thought somebody had me by the neck. So the sleep didn't do me no good. By and by I says to myself, I can't live this way; I'm a-going to find out who it is that's here on the island with me; I'll find it out or bust. Well, I felt better right off.

So I took my paddle and slid out from shore just a step or two, and then let the canoe drop along down amongst the shadows. The moon was shining, and outside of the shadows it made it most as light as day. I poked along well on to an hour, everything still as rocks and sound asleep. Well, by this time I was most down to the foot of the island. A little ripply, cool breeze begun to blow, and that was as good as saying the night was about done. I give her a turn with the paddle and brung her nose to shore; then I got my gun and slipped out and into the edge of the woods. I set down there on a log and looked out through the leaves. I see the moon go off watch and the darkness begin to blanket the river. But in a little while I see a pale streak over the tree-tops and knowed the day was coming. So I took my gun and slipped off towards where I had run across that campfire, stopping every minute or two to listen. But I hadn't no luck somehow; I couldn't seem to find the place. But by and by, sure enough, I catched a glimpse of fire away through the trees. I went for it, cautious and slow. By and by I was close enough to have a look, and there laid a man on the ground. It most give me the fantods. He had a blanket around his head, and his head was nearly in the fire. I set there behind a clump of bushes within about six foot of him and kept my eyes on him steady. It was getting gray daylight now. Pretty soon he gapped and stretched himself and hove off the blanket—and it was Miss Watson's Jim! I bet I was glad to see him. I says:

"Hello, Jim!" and skipped out.

He bounced up and stared at me wild. Then he drops down on his knees and puts his hands together and says:

"Doan' hurt me—don't! I hain't ever done no harm to a ghos'. I alwuz liked dead people, en done all I could for 'em. You go en git in de river agin, whah you b'longs, en doan' do nufin to Ole Jim, 'at 'uz alwuz yo' fren'."

Well, I warn't long making him understand I warn't dead. I was ever so glad to see Jim. I warn't lonesome now. I told him I warn't afraid of *him* telling the people where I was. I talked along but he only set there and looked at me, never said nothing. Then I says:

"It's good daylight. Le's get breakfast. Make up your camp-fire good."

"What's de use er makin' up de campfire to cook strawbries en sich truck? But you got a gun, hain't you? Den we kin git sumfn better den strawbries."

"Strawberries and such truck," I says. "Is that what you live on?"

"I couldn't git nuffn else," he says.

223

"Why, how long you been on the island, Jim?"

"I come heah de night arter you's killed."

"What, all that time?"

"Yes-indeedy."

"And ain't you had nothing but that kind of rubbage to eat?"

"No, sah—nuffn else."

"Well, you must be most starved, ain't you?"

"I reck'n I could eat a hoss. I think I could. How long you ben on de islan'?"

"Since the night I got killed."

"No! W'y, what has you lived on? But you got a gun. Oh, yes, you got a gun. Dat's good. Now you kill sumfn en I'll make up de fire."

So we went over to where the canoe was and while he built a fire in a grassy open place amongst the trees, I fetched meal and bacon and coffee and coffee-pot and frying-pan and sugar and tin cups, and the nigger was set back considerable, because he reckoned it was all done with witchcraft. I catched a good big catfish, too, and Jim cleaned him with his knife and fried him.

When breakfast was ready we lolled on the grass and eat it smoking hot. Jim laid it in with all his might, for he was most about starved. Then when we had got pretty well stuffed, we laid off and lazied.

By and by Jim says:

"But looky here, Huck, who wuz it dat 'uz killed in dat shanty ef it warn't you?"

Then I told him the whole thing, and he said it was smart. He said Tom Sawyer couldn't get up no better plan than what I had. Then I says:

"How do you come to be here, Jim, and how'd you get here?"

He looked pretty uneasy, and didn't say nothing for a minute. Then he says:

"Maybe I better not tell."

"Why, Jim?"

"Well, dey's reasons. But you wouldn't tell on me ef I 'uz to tell you, would you, Huck?"

"Blamed if I would, Jim."

"Well, I b'lieve you, Huck. I—I *run off.*"

"Jim!"

"But mind, you said you wouldn't tell—you know you said you wouldn' tell, Huck."

"Well, I did. I said I wouldn't and I'll stick to it. Honest *injun,* I will. People would call me a low-down Abolitionist and despise me for keeping mum—but that don't make no difference. I ain't a-going to tell, and I ain't a-going back there, anyways. So, now, le's know all about it."

"Well, you see, it 'uz dis way. Ole missus—dat's Miss Watson—she pecks on me all de time, en treats me pooty rough, but she alwuz said she wouldn' sell me down to Orleans. But I noticed dey wuz a nigger trader roun' de place considable lately, en I begin to get oneasy. Well, one night I creeps to de do' pooty late, en de do' warn't quite shet, en I hear ole missus tell de widder she gwyne to sell me down to Orleans, but she didn' want to, but she could get eight hund'd dollars for me, en it 'uz sich a big stack o' money she couldn' resis'. De widder she try to git her to say she wouldn' do it, but I never waited to hear de res'. I lit out mighty quick, I tell you.

"I tuck out en shin down de hill, en 'spec to steal a skift 'long de sho' som'ers 'bove de town, but dey wuz people a-stirring yit, so I hid in de ole tumbledown cooper shop on de bank to wait for everybody to go 'way. Well, I wuz dah all night. Dey wuz somebody roun' all de time. 'Long 'bout six in de mawnin' skifts begin to go by, en 'bout eight er nine every skift dat went 'long wuz talkin' 'bout how yo' pap come over to de town en say you's killed. Dese las' skifts wuz full o' ladies en genlmen a-goin' over for to see de place. Sometimes dey'd pull up at de sho' en take a res' b'fo' dey started acrost, so by de talk I got to know all 'bout de killin'. I 'uz powerful sorry you's killed, Huck, but I ain't no mo' now.

"I laid dah under de shavin's all day. I 'uz hungry but I warn't afeard; bekase I knowed ole missus en de widder wuz goin' to start to de camp-meet'n' right arter breakfas' en be gone all day, en dey knows I goes off wid de cattle 'bout daylight, so dey wouldn' 'spec to see me roun' de place, en so dey wouldn' miss me tell arter dark in de evenin'. De yuther servants wouldn' miss me, kase dey'd shin out en take holiday soon as de ole folks 'uz out'n de way.

"Well, when it come dark I tuck out up de river road, en went 'bout two mile er more to whah dey warn't no houses. I'd made up my mine 'bout what I's a-gwyne to do. You see, ef I kep' on tryin' to git away afoot, de dogs 'ud track me; ef I stole a skift to cross over, dey'd miss dat skift, you see, en dey'd know 'bout what I'd lan' on de yuther side, en whah to pick up my track. So I says, a raff is what I's arter; it doan' *make* no track.

"I see a light a-comin' roun' de p'int bymeby, so I wade' in en shove' a log ahead o' me en swum more'n halfway acrost de river, en got in 'mongst de driftwood, en kep' my head down low, en kinder swum agin de current tell de raff come along. Den I swum to de stern uv it en tuck a-holt. It clouded up en 'uz pooty dark for a little while. So I clumb up en laid down on de planks. De men 'uz all 'way yonder in de middle, whah de lantern wuz. De river wuz a-risin', en dey wuz a good current; so I reck'n'd 'at by fo' in de mawnin' I'd be twenty-five mile down de river, en den I'd slip in jis' b'fo' daylight en swim asho', en take to de woods on de Illinois side.

226

"But I didn' have no luck. When we 'uz mos' down to de head er de islan' a man begin to come aft wid de lantern. I see it warn't no use fer to wait, so I slid overboard en struck out fer de islan'. Well, I had a notion I could lan' mos' anywhers, but I couldn'—bank too bluff. I 'uz mos' to de foot er de islan' b'fo' I foun' a good place. I went into de woods en jedged I wouldn' fool wid raffs no mo', long as dey move de lantern roun' so. I had my pipe en a plug er dog-leg en some matches in my cap, en dey warn't wet, so I 'uz all right."

"And so you ain't had no meat nor bread to eat all this time? Why didn't you get mud-turkles?"

"How you gwyne to git 'm? You can't slip up on um en grab um; en how's a body gwyne to hit um wid a rock? How could a body do it in de night? En I warn't gwyne to show myself on de bank in de daytime."

"Well, that's so. You've had to keep in the woods all the time, of course. Did you hear 'em shooting the cannon?"

"Oh, yes. I knowed dey was arter you. I see um go by heah—watched um thoo de bushes."

Some young birds come along, flying a yard or two at a time and lighting. Jim said it was a sign it was going to rain. He said it was a sign when young chickens flew that way, and so he reckoned it was the same way when young birds done it. I was going to catch some of them but Jim wouldn't let me. He said it was death. He said his father laid mighty sick once and some of them catched a bird, and his old granny said his father would die, and he did.

And Jim said you mustn't count the things you are going to cook for dinner, because that would bring bad luck. The same if you shook the tablecloth after sun-down. And he said if a man owned a beehive and that man died, the bees must be told about it before sun-up next morning, or else the bees would all weaken down and quit work and die. Jim said bees wouldn't sting idiots; but I didn't believe that, because I had tried them lots of times myself, and they wouldn't sting me.

I had heard about some of these things before, but not all of them. Jim knowed all kinds of signs. He said he knowed most everything. I said it looked to me like all the signs was about bad luck, and so I asked him if there warn't any good-luck signs. He says:

"Mighty few—an' *dey* ain't no use to a body. What you want to know when good luck's a-comin' for? Want to keep it off?" And he said: "Ef you's got hairy arms en a hairy breas', it's a sign dat you's a-gwyne to be rich. Well, dey's some use in a sign like dat, 'kase it's so fur ahead. You see, maybe you's got to be po' a long time fust, en so you might git discourage' en kill yo'sef 'f you didn' know by de sign dat you gwyne to be rich bymeby."

"Have you got hairy arms and a hairy breast, Jim?"

"What's de use to ax dat question? Doan' you see I has?"

"Well, are you rich?"

"No, but I ben rich wunst, and gwyne to be rich agin. Wunst I had fo'teen dollars, but I tuck to specalat'n', en got busted out."

"What did you speculate in, Jim?"

"Well, fust I tackled stock."

"What kind of stock?"

"Why, live stock—cattle, you know. I put ten dollars in a cow. But I ain' gwyne to resk no mo' money in stock. De cow up 'n' died on my han's."

"So you lost the ten dollars."

"No, I didn' lose it all. I on'y los' 'bout nine of it. I sole de hide en taller for a dollar en ten cents."

"You had five dollars and ten cents left. Did you speculate any more?"

"Yes. You know dat one-laigged nigger dat b'longs to old Misto Bradish? Well, he sot up a bank, en say anybody dat put in a dollar would git fo' dollars mo' at de en' er de year. Well, all de niggers went in but dey didn' have much. I wuz de on'y one dat had much. So I stuck out for mo' dan fo' dollars, en I said 'f I didn' git it I'd start a bank myself. Well, o' course dat nigger want' to keep me out er de business, bekase he says dey warn't business 'nough for two banks, so he say I could put in my five dollars en he pay me thirty-five at de en' er de year.

"So I done it. Den I reck'n'd I'd inves' de thirty-five dollars right off en keep things a-movin'. Dey wuz a nigger name' Bob, dat had ketched a wood-flat, en his marster didn' know it; en I bought it off'n him en told him to take de thirty-five dollars when de en' er de year come; but somebody stole de wood-flat dat night, en nex' day de one-laigged nigger say de bank's busted. So dey didn' none uv us git no money."

"What did you do with the ten cents, Jim?"

"Well, I'uz gwyne to spen' it but I had a dream, en de dream tole me to give it to a nigger name' Balum—Balum's Ass dey call him for short; he's one er dem chuckleheads, you know. But he's lucky, dey say, en I see I warn't lucky. De dream say let Balum inves' de ten cents en he'd make a raise for me. Well, Balum he tuck de money, en when he wuz in church he hear de preacher say dat whoever give to de po' len' to de Lord, en boun' to git his money back a hund'd times. So Balum he tuck en give de ten cents to de po', en laid low to see what wuz gwyne to come of it."

"Well, what did come of it, Jim?"

"Nuffn never come of it. I couldn' manage to k'lect dat money no way; en Balum he couldn'. I ain' gwyne to len' no mo' money 'dout I see de security. Boun' to git yo' money

229

back a hund'd times, de preacher says! Ef I could git de ten *cents* back, I'd call it squah, en be glad er de chanst."

"Well, it's all right anyway, Jim, long as you're going to be rich again some time or other."

"Yes; en I's rich now, come to look at it. I owns mysef, en I's wuth eight hund'd dollars. I wisht I had de money, I wouldn' want no mo'."

CHAPTER 9

THE HOUSE OF DEATH FLOATS BY

I wanted to go and look at a place right about the middle of the island that I'd found when I was exploring; so we started and soon got to it, because the island was only three miles long and a quarter of a mile wide.

This place was a tolerable long, steep hill or ridge about forty foot high. We had a rough time getting to the top, the sides was so steep and the bushes so thick. We tramped and clumb around all over it and by and by found a good big cavern in the rock, most up to the top on the side towards Illinois. The cavern was as big as two or three rooms bunched together and Jim could stand up straight in it. It was cool in there. Jim was for putting our traps in there right away but I said we didn't want to be climbing up and down there all the time.

Jim said if we had the canoe hid in a good place and had all the traps in the cavern, we could rush there if anybody was to come to the island and they would never find us without dogs. And, besides, he said them little birds had said it was going to rain, and did I want the things to get wet?

So we went back and got the canoe and paddled up abreast the cavern, and lugged all the traps up there. Then we hunted up a place close by to hide the canoe in, amongst the thick willows. We took some fish off of the lines and set them again and begun to get ready for dinner.

The door of the cavern was big enough to roll a hogshead in, and on one side of the door the floor stuck out a little bit and was flat and a good place to build a fire on. So we built it there and cooked dinner.

We spread the blankets inside for a carpet, and eat our dinner in there. We put all the other things handy at the back of the cavern. Pretty soon it darkened up and begun to thunder and lighten; so the birds was right about it. Directly it begun to rain and it rained like all fury, too, and I never see the wind blow so. It was one of these regular summer storms. It would get so dark that it looked all blue-black outside, and lovely; and the rain would thrash along by so thick that the trees off a little ways looked dim and spider-webby; and here would come a blast of wind that would bend the trees down and turn up the pale underside of the leaves; and then a perfect ripper of a gust would follow along and set the branches to tossing their arms as if they was just wild; and next, when it was just about the bluest and blackest—*fst!* it was as bright as glory and you'd have a little glimpse of tree-tops a-plunging about away off yonder in the storm, hundreds of yards further than you could see before; dark as sin again in a second and now you'd hear the thunder let go with an awful crash and then go rumbling, grumbling, tumbling down the sky towards the under side of the world, like rolling empty barrels downstairs—where it's long stairs and they bounce a good deal, you know.

"Jim, this is nice," I says. "I wouldn't want to be nowhere else but here. Pass me along another hunk of fish and some hot corn-bread."

"Well, you wouldn' 'a' ben here 'f it hadn't 'a' ben for Jim. You'd 'a' ben down dah in de woods widout any dinner, en gittin' mos' drownded, too; dat you would, honey. Chickens knows when it's gwyne to rain, en so do de birds, chile."

The river went on raising and raising for ten or twelve days, till at last it was over the banks. The water was three or four foot deep on the island in the low places and on the Illinois bottom. On that side it was a good many miles wide but on the Missouri side it was the same old distance across—a half a mile—because the Missouri shore was just a wall of high bluffs.

Daytimes we paddled all over the island in the canoe. It was mighty cool and shady in the deep woods, even if the sun was blazing outside. We went winding in and out amongst the trees and sometimes the vines hung so thick we had to back away and go some other way. Well, on every old broken-down tree you could see rabbits and snakes and such things, and when the island had been overflowed a day or two they got so tame, on account of being hungry, that you could paddle right up and put your hand on them if you wanted to, but not the snakes and turtles—they would slide off in the water. The ridge our cavern was in was full of them. We could 'a' had pets enough if we'd wanted them.

One night we catched a little section of a lumber-raft—nice pine planks. It was twelve foot wide and about fifteen or sixteen foot long, and the top stood above water six or seven inches—a solid, level floor. We could see saw-logs go by in the daylight sometimes but we let them go; we didn't show ourselves in daylight.

Another night when we was up at the head of the island just before daylight, here comes a frame house down, on the west side. She was a two-story, and tilted over considerable. We paddled out and got aboard—clumb in at an upstairs window. But it was too dark to see yet, so we made the canoe fast and set in her to wait for daylight.

The light begun to come before we got to the foot of the island. Then we looked in at the window. We could make out a bed and a table and two old chairs and lots of things around about on the floor, and there was clothes hanging against the wall. There was something laying on the floor in the far corner that looked like a man. So Jim says:

"Hello, you!"

But it didn't budge. So I hollered again, and then Jim says:

"De man ain't asleep—he's dead. You hold still—I'll go en see."

He went and bent down and looked, and says:

"It's a dead man. Yes, indeedy; naked, too. He's ben shot in de back. I reck'n he's ben dead two er three days. Come in, Huck, but doan' look at his face—it's too gashly."

I didn't look at him at all. Jim throwed some old rags over him, but he needn't done it; I didn't want to see him. There was heaps of old greasy cards scattered around over the floor and old whisky-bottles and a couple of masks made out of black cloth; and all over the walls was the ignorantest kind of words and pictures made with charcoal. There was two old dirty calico dresses and a sun-bonnet and some women's underclothes hanging against the wall, and some men's clothing, too. We put the lot into the canoe; it might come good. There was a boy's old speckled straw hat on the floor; I took that, too. And there was a bottle that had had milk in it and it had a rag stopper for a baby to suck. We would 'a' took the bottle but it was broke. There was a seedy old chest and an old hair trunk with the hinges broke. They stood open but there warn't nothing left in them that was any account. The way things was scattered about we reckoned the people left in a hurry and warn't fixed so as to carry off most of their stuff.

We got an old tin lantern, and a butcher-knife without any handle, and a bran-new Barlow knife worth two bits in any store, and a lot of tallow candles, and a tin candle-stick, and a gourd, and a tin cup, and a ratty old bed-quilt off the bed, and a reticule with needles and pins and beeswax and buttons and thread and all such truck in it, and a hatchet and some nails, and a fish-line as thick as my little finger with some monstrous hooks on it, and a roll of buckskin, and a leather dog-collar, and a horseshoe, and some vials of medicine that didn't have no label on them; and just as we was leaving I found a tolerable good currycomb and Jim he found a ratty old fiddle-bow and a wooden leg. The straps was broke off of it but, barring that, it was a good enough leg, though it was too long for me and not long enough for Jim, and we couldn't find the other one, though we hunted all around.

And so, take it all around, we made a good haul. When we was ready to shove off we was a quarter of a mile below the island and it was pretty broad day; so I made Jim lay down in the canoe and cover up with the quilt, because if he set up people could tell he was a nigger a good ways off. I paddled over to the Illinois shore and drifted down most a half a mile doing it. I crept up the dead water under the bank and hadn't no accidents and didn't see nobody. We got home all safe.

CHAPTER 10

WHAT COMES OF HANDLIN' SNAKE-SKIN

After breakfast I wanted to talk about the dead man and guess out how he come to be killed but Jim didn't want to. He said it would fetch bad luck and besides, he said, he might come and ha'nt us; he said a man that warn't buried was more likely to go a-ha'nting around than one that was planted and comfortable. That sounded pretty reasonable, so I didn't say no more; but I couldn't keep from studying over it and wishing I knowed who shot the man and what they done it for.

We rummaged the clothes we'd got and found eight dollars in silver sewed up in the lining of an old blanket overcoat. Jim said he reckoned the people in that house stole the coat, because if they'd 'a' knowed the money was there they wouldn't 'a' left it. I said I reckoned they killed him, too, but Jim didn't want to talk about that. I says:

"Now you think it's bad luck; but what did you say when I fetched in the snake-skin that I found on the top of the ridge day before yesterday? You said it was the worst bad luck in the world to touch a snake-skin with my hands. Well, here's your bad luck! We've raked in all this truck and eight dollars besides. I wish we could have some bad luck like this every day, Jim."

"Never you mind, honey, never you mind. Don't you git too peart. It's a-comin'. Mind I tell you, it's a-comin'."

It did come, too. It was a Tuesday that we had that talk. Well, after dinner Friday we was laying around in the grass at the upper end of the ridge, and got out of tobacco. I went to the cavern to get some and found a rattlesnake in there. I killed him and curled him up on the foot of Jim's blanket, ever so natural, thinking there'd be some fun when Jim found him there. Well, by night I forgot all about the snake, and when Jim flung himself down on the blanket while I struck a light the snake's mate was there, and bit him.

He jumped up yelling, and the first thing the light showed was the varmint curled up and ready for another spring. I laid him out in a second with a stick, and Jim grabbed pap's whisky-jug and begun to pour it down.

He was barefooted and the snake bit him right on the heel. That all comes of my being such a fool as to not remember that wherever you leave a dead snake its mate always comes there and curls around it. Jim told me to chop off the snake's head and throw it away and then skin the body and roast a piece of it. I done it, and he eat it and said it would help cure him. He made me take off the rattles and tie them around his wrist, too. He said that that would help. Then I slid out quiet and throwed the snakes clear away amongst the bushes; for I warn't going to let Jim find out it was all my fault, not if I could help it.

Jim sucked and sucked at the jug and now and then he got out of his head and pitched around and yelled, but every time he come to himself he went to sucking at the jug again. His foot swelled up pretty big and so did his leg but by and by the drunk begun to come and so I judged he was all right, but I'd druther been bit with a snake than pap's whisky.

Jim was laid up for four days and nights. Then the swelling was all gone and he was around again. I made up my mind I wouldn't ever take a-holt of a snake-skin again with my hands, now that I see what had come of it. Jim said he reckoned I would believe him next time. And he said that handling a snake-skin was such awful bad luck that maybe we hadn't got to the end of it yet. He said he druther see the new moon over his left shoulder as much as a thousand times then take up a snake-skin in his hand. Well, I was getting to feel that way myself, though I've always reckoned that looking at the new moon over your left shoulder is one of the carelessest and foolishest things a body can do. Old Hank Bunker done it once, and bragged about it, and in less than two years he got drunk and fell off of the shot-tower and spread himself out so that he was just a kind of a layer, as you may say, and they slid him edgeways between two barn doors for a coffin and buried him so, so they say, but I didn't see it. Pap told me. But anyway it all come of looking at the moon that way, like a fool.

Well, the days went along, and the river went down between its banks again, and about the first thing we done was to bait one of the big hooks with a skinned rabbit and set it and catch a catfish that was as big as a man, being six foot two inches long, and weighed over two hundred pounds. We couldn't handle him, of course; he would 'a' flung us into Illinois. We just set there and watched him rip and tear around till he drownded. We found a brass button in his stomach and a round ball and lots of rubbage. We split the ball open with the hatchet and there was a spool in it. Jim said he'd had it there a long time, to coat it over so and make a ball of it. It was as big a fish as was ever catched in the Mississippi, I reckon. Jim said he hadn't ever seen a bigger one. He would 'a' been worth a good deal over at the village. They peddle out such a fish as that by the pound in the market-house there; everybody buys some of him; his meat's as white as snow and makes a good fry.

Next morning I said it was getting slow and dull, and I wanted to get a stirring-up some way. I said I reckoned I would slip over the river and find out what was going on. Jim liked that notion, but he said I must go in the dark and look sharp. Then he studied it over and said, couldn't I put on some of them old things and dress up like a girl? That was a good notion, too. So we shortened up one of the calico gowns and I turned up my trouser-legs to my knees and got into it. Jim hitched it behind with the hooks and it was a fair fit. I put on the sun-bonnet and tied it under my chin, and then for a body to look in and see my face was like looking down a joint of stove-pipe. Jim said nobody would know me, even in the daytime, hardly. I practiced around all day to get the hang of the things, and by and by I could do pretty well in them, only Jim said I didn't walk like a girl, and he said I must quit pulling up my gown to get at my britches-pocket. I took notice and done better.

I started up the Illinois shore in the canoe just after dark.

I started across to the town from a little below the ferry-landing, and the drift of the current fetched me in at the bottom of the town. I tied up and started along the bank. There was a light burning in a little shanty that hadn't been lived in for a long time, and I wondered who had took up quarters there. I slipped up and peeped in at the window. There was a woman about forty year old in there knitting by a candle that was on a pine table. I didn't know her face; she was a stranger, for you couldn't start a face in that town that I didn't know. Now this was lucky, because I was weakening; I was getting afraid people might know my voice and find me out. But if this woman had been in such a little town two days she could tell me all I wanted to know; so I knocked at the door, and made up my mind I wouldn't forget I was a girl.

CHAPTER 11

THEY'RE AFTER US!

"Come in," says the woman, and I did. She says: "Take a cheer."

I done it. She looked me all over with her little shiny eyes, and says:

"What might your name be?"

"Sarah Williams."

"Where'bouts do you live? In this neighborhood?"

"No'm. In Hookerville, seven mile below. I've walked all the way and I'm all tired out."

"Hungry, too, I reckon. I'll find you something."

"No'm, I ain't hungry. I was so hungry I had to stop two mile below here at a farm; so I ain't hungry no more. It's what makes me so late. My mother's down sick and out of money and everything, and I come to tell my uncle Abner Moore. He lives at the upper end of the town, she says. I hain't ever been here before. Do you know him?"

"No; but I don't know everybody yet. I haven't lived here quite two weeks. It's a considerable ways to the upper end of the town. You better stay here all night. Take off your bonnet."

"No," I says; "I'll rest awhile, I reckon, and go on. I ain't afeard of the dark."

She said she wouldn't let me go by myself, but her husband would be in by and by, maybe in a hour and a half, and she'd send him along with me. Then she got to talking about her husband, and about her relations up the river, and her relations down the river, and about how much better off they used to was, and how they didn't know but they'd made a mistake coming to our town, instead of letting well alone—and so on and so on, till I was afeard *I* had made a mistake coming to her to find out what was going on in the town; but by and by she dropped on to pap and the murder and then I was pretty willing to let her clatter right along. She told about me and Tom Sawyer finding the twelve thousand dollars (only she got it twenty) and all about pap and what a hard lot he was, and what a hard lot I was, and at last she got down to where I was murdered. I says:

"Who done it? We've heard considerable about these goings-on down in Hookerville, but we don't know who 'twas that killed Huck Finn."

"Well, I reckon there's a right smart chance of people *here* that 'd like to know who killed him. Some thinks old Finn done it himself."

"No—is that so?"

239

"Most everybody thought it at first. He'll never know how nigh he come to getting lynched. But before night they changed around and judged it was done by a runaway nigger named Jim."

"Why *he*—"

I stopped. I reckoned I better keep still. She run on, and never noticed I had put in at all:

"The nigger run off the very night Huck Finn was killed. So there's a reward out for him—three hundred dollars. And there's a reward out for old Finn, too—two hundred dollars. You see, he come to town the morning after the murder and told about it, and was out with 'em on the ferryboat hunt, and right away after he up and left. Before night they wanted to lynch him but he was gone, you see. Well, next day they found out the nigger was gone; they found out he hadn't ben seen sence ten o'clock the night the murder was done. So then they put it on him, you see; and while they was full of it, next day, back comes old Finn, and went boo-hooing to Judge Thatcher to get money to hunt for the nigger all over Illinois with. The judge give him some, and that evening he got drunk and was around till after midnight with a couple of mighty hard-looking strangers, and then went off with them. Well, he hain't come back sence and they ain't looking for him back till this thing blows over a little, for people thinks now that he killed his boy and fixed things so folks would think robbers done it, and then he'd get Huck's money without having to bother a long time with a lawsuit. People do say he warn't any too good to do it. Oh, he's sly, I reckon. If he don't come back for a year he'll be all right. You can't prove anything on him, you know; everything will be quieted down then, and he'll walk into Huck's money as easy as nothing."

"Yes, I reckon so, 'm. I don't see nothing in the way of it. Has everybody quit thinking the nigger done it?"

"Oh, no, not everybody. A good many thinks he done it. But they'll get the nigger pretty soon now, and maybe they can scare it out of him."

"Why, are they after him yet?"

"Well, you're innocent, ain't you! Does three hundred dollars lay around every day for people to pick up? Some folks think the nigger ain't far from here. I'm one of them—but I hain't talked it around. A few days ago I was talking with an old couple that lives next door in the log shanty, and they happened to say hardly anybody ever goes to that island over yonder that they call Jackson's Island. Don't anybody live there? says I. No, nobody, says they. I didn't say any more but I done some thinking. I was pretty near certain I'd seen smoke over there, about the head of the island, a day or two before that, so I says to myself, like as not that nigger's hiding over there; anyway, says I, it's worth the trouble to give the place a hunt. I hain't seen any smoke sence, so I reckon maybe he's gone, if it was him; but husband's going over to see—him and another man. He was gone up the river; but he got back today, and I told him as soon as he got here two hours ago."

I had got so uneasy I couldn't set still. I had to do something with my hands; so I took up a needle off of the table and went to threading it. My hands shook and I was making a bad job of it. When the woman stopped talking I looked up, and she was looking at me pretty curious and smiling a little. I put down the needle and thread and let on to be interested—and I was, too—and says:

"Three hundred dollars is a power of money. I wish my mother could get it. Is your husband going over there tonight?"

"Oh, yes. He went up-town with the man I was telling you of, to get a boat and see if they could borrow another gun. They'll go over after midnight."

241

"Couldn't they see better if they was to wait till daytime?"

"Yes. And couldn't the nigger see better, too? After midnight he'll likely be asleep and they can slip around through the woods and hunt up his campfire all the better for the dark, if he's got one."

"I didn't think of that."

The woman kept looking at me pretty curious, and I didn't feel a bit comfortable. Pretty soon she says:

"What did you say your name was, honey?"

"M—Mary Williams."

Somehow it didn't seem to me that I said it was Mary before, so I didn't look up—seemed to me I said it was Sarah; so I felt sort of cornered and was afeard maybe I was looking it, too. I wished the woman would say something more; the longer she set still the uneasier I was. But now she says:

"Honey, I thought you said it was Sarah when you first come in?"

"Oh, yes'm, I did. Sarah Mary Williams. Sarah's my first name. Some calls me Sarah, some calls me Mary."

"Oh, that's the way of it?"

"Yes'm."

I was feeling better then but I wished I was out of there, anyway. I couldn't look up yet.

Well, the woman fell to talking about how hard times was, and how poor they had to live, and how the rats was as free as if they owned the place, and so forth and so on, and then I got easy again. She was right about the rats. You'd see one stick his nose out of a hole in the corner every little while. She said she had to have things handy to throw at them when she was alone, or they wouldn't give her no peace. She showed me a bar of lead twisted up into a knot and said she was a good shot with it generly, but she'd wrenched her arm a day or two ago and didn't know whether she could throw true now. But she watched for a chance and directly banged away at a rat, but she missed him wide and said, "Ouch!" it hurt her arm so. Then she told me to try for the next one. I wanted to be getting away before the old man got back, but of course I didn't let on. I got the thing, and the first rat that showed his nose I let drive, and if he'd 'a' stayed where he was he'd 'a' been a tolerable sick rat. She said that was first-rate and she reckoned I would hive the next one. She went and got the lump of lead and fetched it back, and brought along a hank of yarn which she wanted me to help her with. I held up my two hands and she put the hank over them, and went on talking about her and her husband's matters. But she broke off to say:

"Keep your eye on the rats. You better have the lead in your lap, handy."

So she dropped the lump into my lap just at that moment, and I clapped my legs together on it and she went on talking. But only about a minute. Then she took off the hank and looked me straight in the face, but very pleasant, and says:

"Come, now, what's your real name?"

"Wh-what, mum?"

"What's your real name? Is it Bill, or Tom, or Bob?—or what is it?"

I reckon I shook like a leaf and I didn't know hardly what to do. But I says:

"Please to don't poke fun at a poor girl like me, mum. If I'm in the way here, I'll—"

"No, you won't. Set down and stay where you are. I ain't going to hurt you and I ain't going to tell on you, nuther. You just tell me your secret, and trust me. I'll keep it; and, what's more, I'll help you. So'll my old man if you want him to. You see, you're a runaway 'prentice, that's all. It ain't anything. There ain't no harm in it. You've been treated bad and you made up your mind to cut. Bless you, child, I wouldn't tell on you. Tell me all about it now, that's a good boy."

So I said it wouldn't be no use to try to play it any longer, and I would just make a clean breast and tell her everything but she mustn't go back on her promise. Then I told her my father and mother was dead and the law had bound me out to a mean old farmer in the country thirty mile back from the river, and he treated me so bad I couldn't stand it no longer; he went away to be gone a couple of days and so I took my chance and stole some of his daughter's old clothes and cleared out, and I had been three nights coming the thirty miles. I traveled nights and hid daytimes and slept, and the bag of bread and meat I carried from home lasted me all the way, and I had a-plenty. I said I believed my uncle Abner Moore would take care of me, and so that was why I struck out for this town of Goshen.

"Goshen, child? This ain't Goshen. This is St. Petersburg. Goshen's ten mile further up the river. Who told you this was Goshen?"

"Why, a man I met at daybreak this morning, just as I was going to turn into the woods for my regular sleep. He told me when the roads forked I must take the right hand, and five mile would fetch me to Goshen."

"He was drunk, I reckon. He told you just exactly wrong."

"Well, he did act like he was drunk but it ain't no matter now. I got to be moving along. I'll fetch Goshen before daylight."

"Hold on a minute. I'll put you up a snack to eat. You might want it."

So she put me up a snack, and says:

"Say, when a cow's laying down, which end of her gets up first? Answer up prompt now—don't stop to study over it. Which end gets up first?"

"The hind end, mum."

"Well, then, a horse?"

"The for'rard end, mum."

"Which side of a tree does the moss grow on?"

"North side."

"If fifteen cows is browsing on a hillside, how many of them eats with their heads pointed the same direction?"

"The whole fifteen, mum."

"Well, I reckon you *have* lived in the country. I thought maybe you was trying to hocus me again. What's your real name, now?"

"George Peters, mum."

"Well, try to remember it, George. Don't forget and tell me it's Elexander before you go, and then get out by saying it's George Elexander when I catch you. And don't go about women in that old calico. You do a girl tolerable poor but you might fool men, maybe. Bless you, child, when you set out to thread a needle don't hold the thread still and fetch the needle up to it; hold the needle still and poke the thread at it; that's the way a woman most always does but a man always does t'other way. And when you throw at a rat or anything, hitch yourself up a-tiptoe and fetch your hand up over your head as awkward as you can and miss your rat about six or seven foot. Throw stiffarmed from the shoulder, like there was a pivot there for it to turn on, like a girl, not from the wrist and elbow, with your arm out to one side, like a boy. And, mind you, when a girl tries to catch anything in her lap she throws her knees apart; she don't clap them together, the way you did when you catched the lump of lead. Why, I spotted you for a boy when you was threading the needle and I contrived the other things just to make certain. Now trot along to your uncle, Sarah Mary Williams George Elexander Peters, and if you get into trouble you send word to Mrs. Judith Loftus, which is me, and I'll do what I can to get you out of it. Keep the river road all the way and next time you tramp take shoes and socks with you. The river road's a rocky one, and your feet'll be in a condition when you get to Goshen, I reckon."

I went up the bank about fifty yards, and then I doubled on my tracks and slipped back to where my canoe was, a good piece below the house. I jumped in and was off in a hurry. I went upstream far enough to make the head of the island, and then started across. I took off the sun-bonnet, for I didn't want no blinders on then. When I was about the middle I heard the clock begin to strike, so I stops and listens; the sound come faint over the water but clear—eleven. When I struck the head of the island I never waited to blow, though I was most winded, but I shoved right into the timber where my old camp used to be, and started a good fire there on a high and dry spot.

Then I jumped in the canoe and dug out for our place, a mile and a half below, as hard as I could go. I landed, and slopped through the timber and up the ridge and into the cavern. There Jim laid, sound asleep on the ground. I roused him out and says:

"Git up and hump yourself, Jim! There ain't a minute to lose. They're after us!"

Jim never asked no questions, he never said a word, but the way he worked for the next half an hour showed about how he was scared. By that time everything we had in the world was on our raft and she was ready to be shoved out from the willow cove where she was hid. We put out the campfire at the cavern the first thing, and didn't show a candle outside after that.

I took the canoe out from the shore a little piece and took a look; but if there was a boat around I couldn't see it, for stars and shadows ain't good to see by. Then we got out the raft and slipped along down in the shade, past the foot of the island dead still—never saying a word.

CHAPTER 12

"BETTER LET BLAME' WELL ALONE"

It must 'a' been close on to one o'clock when we got below the island at last, and the raft did seem to go mighty slow. If a boat was to come along we was going to take to the canoe and break for the Illinois shore; and it was well a boat didn't come, for we hadn't ever thought to put the gun in the canoe, or a fishing-line, or anything to eat. We was in ruther too much of a sweat to think of so many things. It warn't good judgment to put *everything* on the raft.

If the men went to the island I just expect they found the campfire I built and watched it all night for Jim to come. Anyways, they stayed away from us, and if my building the fire never fooled them it warn't no fault of mine. I played it as low-down on them as I could.

When the first streak of day begun to show we tied up to a towhead in a big bend on the Illinois side, and hacked off cottonwood branches with the hatchet, and covered up the raft with them so she looked like there had been a cave-in in the bank there. A towhead is a sand-bar that has cottonwoods on it as thick as harrow-teeth.

We had mountains on the Missouri shore and heavy timber on the Illinois side, and the channel was down the Missouri shore at that place, so we warn't afraid of anybody running across us. We laid there all day, and watched the rafts and steamboats spin down the Missouri shore, and up-bound steamboats fight the big river in the middle. I told Jim all about the time I had jabbering with that woman; and Jim said she was a smart one, and if she was to start after us herself *she* wouldn't set down and watch a campfire—no, sir, she'd fetch a dog. Well, then, I said, why couldn't she tell her husband to fetch a dog? Jim said he bet she did think of it by the time the men was ready to start, and he believed they must 'a' gone up-town to get a dog and so they lost all that time, or else we wouldn't be here on a towhead sixteen or seventeen mile below the village—no, indeedy, we would be in that same old town again. So I said I didn't care what was the reason they didn't get us as long as they didn't.

When it was beginning to come on dark we poked our heads out of the cottonwood thicket, and looked up and down and across; nothing in sight; so Jim took up some of the top planks of the raft and built a snug wigwam to get under in blazing weather and rainy, and to keep the things dry. Jim made a floor for the wigwam and raised it a foot or more above the level of the raft, so now the blankets and all the traps was out of reach of steamboat waves. Right in the middle of the wigwam we made a layer of dirt about five or six inches deep with a frame around it for to hold it to its place; this was to build a fire on in sloppy weather or chilly; the wigwam would keep it from being seen. We made an extra steering-oar, too, because one of the others might get broke on a snag or something. We fixed up a short forked stick to hang the old lantern on, because we must always light the lantern whenever we see a steamboat coming downstream, to keep from getting run over; but we wouldn't have to light it for upstream boats unless we see we was in what they call a "crossing"; for the river was pretty high yet, very low banks being still a little under water, so up-bound boats didn't always run the channel but hunted easy water.

This second night we run between seven and eight hours, with a current that was making over four mile an hour. We catched fish and talked, and we took a swim now and then to keep off sleepiness. It was kind of solemn, drifting down the big, still river, laying on our backs looking up at the stars, and we didn't ever feel like talking loud and it warn't often that we laughed—only a little kind of a low chuckle. We had mighty good weather as a general thing and nothing ever happened to us at all—that night, nor the next, nor the next.

Every night we passed towns, some of them away up on black hillsides, nothing but just a shiny bed of lights; not a house could you see. The fifth night we passed St. Louis and it was like the whole world lit up. In St. Petersburg they used to say there was twenty or thirty thousand people in St. Louis, but I never believed it till I see that wonderful spread of lights at two o'clock that still night. There warn't a sound there; everybody was asleep.

Every night now I used to slip ashore towards ten o'clock at some little village, and buy ten or fifteen cents' worth of meal or bacon or other stuff to eat; and sometimes I lifted a chicken that warn't roosting comfortable and took him along. Pap always said, take a chicken when you get a chance, because if you don't want him yourself you can easy find somebody that does, and a good deed ain't forgot. I never see pap when he didn't want the chicken himself but that is what he used to say, anyway.

Mornings before daylight I slipped into corn-fields and borrowed a watermelon or a mushmelon or a punkin, or some new corn or things of that kind. Pap always said it warn't no harm to borrow things if you was meaning to pay them back some time, but the widow said it warn't anything but a soft name for stealing and no decent body would do it. Jim said he reckoned the widow was partly right and pap was partly right, so the best way would be for us to pick out two or three things from the list and say we wouldn't borrow them any-

249

more—then he reckoned it wouldn't be no harm to borrow the others. So we talked it over all one night, drifting along down the river, trying to make up our minds whether to drop the watermelons or the canteloupes or the mushmelons, or what. But towards daylight we got it all settled satisfactory and concluded to drop crabapples and p'simmons. We warn't feeling just right before that but it was all comfortable now. I was glad the way it come out, too, because crabapples ain't ever good and the p'simmons wouldn't be ripe for two or three months yet.

We shot a waterfowl now and then that got up too early in the morning or didn't go to bed early enough in the evening. Take it all around, we lived pretty high.

The fifth night below St. Louis we had a big storm after midnight, with a power of thunder and lightning, and the rain poured down in a solid sheet. We stayed in the wigwam and let the raft take care of itself. When the lightning glared out we could see a big straight river ahead, and high, rocky bluffs on both sides. By and by says I, "Hel-*lo*, Jim, looky yonder!" It was a steamboat that had killed herself on a rock. We was drifting straight down for her. The lightning showed her very distinct. She was leaning over, with part of her upper deck above water, and you could see every little chimbly-guy clean and clear, and a chair by the big bell, with an old slouch hat hanging on the back of it, when the flashes come.

Well, it being away in the night and stormy and all so mysterious-like, I felt just the way any other boy would 'a' felt when I seen that wreck laying there so mournful and lonesome in the middle of the river. I wanted to get aboard of her and slink around a little, and see what there was there. So I says:

"Le's land on her, Jim."

But Jim was dead against it at first. He says:

"I doan' want to go fool'n' 'long er no wrack. We's doin' blame' well, en we better let blame' well alone, as de good book says. Like as not dey's a watchman on dat wrack."

"Watchman your grandmother," I says; "there ain't nothing to watch but the texas and the pilot-house, and do you reckon anybody's going to resk his life for a texas and a pilot-house such a night as this, when it's likely to break up and wash off down the river any minute?" Jim couldn't say nothing to that, so he didn't try. "And besides," I says, "we might borrow something worth having out of the captain's stateroom. Seegars, *I* bet you—and cost five cents apiece, solid cash. Steamboat captains is always rich and get sixty dollars a month, and *they* don't care a cent what a thing costs, you know, long as they want it. Stick a candle in your pocket; I can't rest, Jim, till we give her a rummaging. Do you reckon Tom Sawyer would ever go by this thing? Not for pie, he wouldn't. He'd call it an adventure—that's what he'd call it, and he'd land on that wreck if it was his last act. And wouldn't he throw style into it?—wouldn't he spread himself, nor nothing? Why, you'd think it was Christopher C'lumbus discovering Kingdom Come. I wish Tom Sawyer *was* here."

Jim he grumbled a little but give in. He said we mustn't talk any more than we could help, and then talk mighty low. The lightning showed us the wreck again just in time, and we fetched the stabboard derrick and made fast there.

The deck was high out, here. We went sneaking down the slope of it to labboard in the dark, towards the texas, feeling our way slow with our feet and spreading our hands out to fend off the guys, for it was so dark we couldn't see no sign of them. Pretty soon we struck the forward end of the skylight and clumb on to it, and the next step fetched us in front of the captain's door, which was open, and by Jimminy, away down through the texas-hall we see a light! and all in the same second we seem to hear low voices in yonder!

Jim whispered and said he was feeling powerful sick, and told me to come along. I says, all right, and was going to start for the raft, but just then I heard a voice wail out and say:

"Oh, please don't, boys; I swear I won't ever tell!"

Another voice said, pretty loud:

"It's a lie, Jim Turner. You've acted this way before. You always want more'n your share of the truck and you've always got it, too, because you've swore 't if you didn't you'd tell. But this time you've said it jest one time too many. You're the meanest, treacherousest hound in this country."

By this time Jim was gone for the raft. I was just a-biling with curiosity, and I says to myself, Tom Sawyer wouldn't back out now and so I won't either; I'm a-going to see what's going on here. So I dropped on my hands and knees in the little passage, and crept aft in the dark till there warn't but one stateroom betwixt me and the cross-hall of the texas. Then in there I see a man stretched on the floor and tied hand and foot and two men standing over him, and one of them had a dim lantern in his hand and the other one had a pistol. This one kept pointing the pistol at the man's head on the floor, and saying:

"I'd *like* to! And I orter, too—a mean skunk!"

The man on the floor would shrivel up and say, "Oh, please don't, Bill; I hain't ever goin' to tell."

And every time he said that the man with the lantern would laugh and say:

" 'Deed you *ain't*! You never said no truer thing 'n that, you bet you." And once he said: "Hear him beg! and yit if we hadn't got the best of him and tied him he'd 'a' killed us both. And what *for*? Jist for noth'n'. Jist because we stood on our *rights*—that's what for. But I lay you ain't a-goin' to threaten nobody anymore, Jim Turner. Put *up* that pistol, Bill."

Bill says:

"I don't want to, Jake Packard. I'm for killin' him—and didn't he kill old Hatfield jist the same way—and don't he deserve it?"

"But I don't *want* him killed, and I've got my reasons for it."

"Bless yo' heart for them words, Jake Packard! I'll never forget you long's I live!" says the man on the floor, sort of blubbering.

Packard didn't take no notice of that but hung up his lantern on a nail and started towards where I was, there in the dark, and motioned Bill to come. I crawfished as fast as I could about two yards, but the boat slanted so that I couldn't make very good time; so to keep from getting run over and catched I crawled into a stateroom on the upper side. The man come a-pawing along in the dark, and when Packard got to my stateroom, he says:

"Here—come in here."

And in he come and Bill after him. But before they got in I was up in the upper berth, cornered, and sorry I come. Then they stood there, with their hands on the ledge of the berth, and talked. I couldn't see them but I could tell where they was by the whisky they'd been having. I was glad I didn't drink whisky, but it wouldn't made such difference anyway, because most of the time they couldn't 'a' treed me because I didn't breathe. I was too scared. And, besides, a body *couldn't* breathe and hear such talk. They talked low and earnest. Bill wanted to kill Turner. He says:

"He's said he'll tell and he will. If we was to give both our shares to him *now* it wouldn't make no difference after the row and the way we've served him. Shore's you're born, he'll turn state's evidence; now you hear *me*. I'm for putting him out of his troubles."

"So'm I," says Packard, very quiet.

"Blame it, I'd sorter begun to think you wasn't. Well, then, that's all right. Le's go and do it."

"Hold on a minute; I hain't had my say yit. You listen to me. Shooting's good but there's quieter ways if the thing's *got* to be done. But what *I* say is this: it ain't good sense to go court'n' around after a halter if you can git at what you're up to in some way that's jist as good and at the same time don't bring you into no resks. Ain't that so?"

"You bet it is. But how you goin' to manage it this time?"

"Well, my idea is this: we'll rustle around and gather up whatever pickin's we've overlooked in the staterooms, and shove for shore and hide the truck. Then we'll wait. Now I say it ain't a-goin' to be more'n two hours befo' this wrack breaks up and washes off down the river. See? He'll be drownded, and won't have nobody to blame for it but his own self. I reckon that's a considerable sight better'n killin' of him. I'm unfavorable to killin' a man as long as you can git aroun' it; it ain't good sense, it ain't good morals. Ain't I right?"

"Yes, I reck'n you are. But s'pose she *don't* break up and wash off?"

"Well, we can wait the two hours anyway and see, can't we?"

"All right, then; come along."

So they started, and I lit out, all in a cold sweat, and scrambled forward. It was dark as pitch there; but I said, in a kind of a coarse whisper, "Jim!" and he answered up, right at my elbow, with a sort of a moan, and I says:

"Quick, Jim, it ain't no time for fooling around and moaning; there's a gang of murderers in yonder, and if we don't hunt up their boat and set her drifting down the river so these fellows can't get away from the wreck there's one of 'em going to be in a bad fix. But if we find their boat we can put *all* of 'em in a bad fix—for the sheriff'll get 'em. Quick—hurry! I'll hunt the labboard side, you hunt the stabboard. You start at the raft, and—"

"Oh, my lordy, lordy! *Raf'*? Dey ain' no raf' no mo'; she done broke loose en gone!—en here we is!"

CHAPTER 13

HONEST LOOT FROM THE "WALTER SCOTT"

Well, I catched my breath and most fainted. Shut up on a wreck with such a gang as that! But it warn't no time to be sentimentering. We'd *got* to find that boat now—had to have it for ourselves. So we went a-quaking and shaking down the stabboard side, and slow work it was, too—seemed a week before we got to the stern. No sign of a boat. Jim said he didn't believe he could go any farther—so scared he hadn't hardly any strength left, he said. But I said, come on, if we get left on this wreck we are in a fix, sure. So on we prowled again. We struck for the stern of the texas and found it, and then scrabbled along forwards on the skylight, hanging on from shutter to shutter, for the edge of the skylight was in the water. When we got pretty close to the cross-hall door there was the skiff, sure enough! I could just barely see her. I felt ever so thankful. In another second I would 'a' been aboard of her, but just then the door opened. One of the men stuck his head out only about a couple of foot from me, and I thought I was gone; but he jerked it in again, and says:

"Heave that blame' lantern out o' sight, Bill!"

He flung a bag of something into the boat, and then got in himself and set down. It was Packard. Then Bill *he* come out and got in. Packard says, in a low voice:

"All ready—shove off!"

I couldn't hardly hang on to the shutters, I was so weak. But Bill says:

"Hold on—'d you go through him?"

"No. Didn't you?"

"No. So he's got his share o' the cash yet."

"Well, then, come along; no use to take truck and leave money."

"Say, won't he suspicion what we're up to?"

"Maybe he won't. But we got to have it anyway. Come along."

So they got out and went in.

The door slammed to because it was on the careened side, and in a half second I was in the boat, and Jim come tumbling after me. I out with my knife and cut the rope, and away we went!

We didn't touch an oar and we didn't speak nor whisper, nor hardly even breathe. We went gliding swift along, dead silent, past the tip of the paddle-box and past the stern; then in a second or two more we was a hundred yards below the wreck and the darkness soaked her up, every last sign of her, and we was safe and knowed it.

When we was three or four hundred yards downstream we see the lantern show like a little spark at the texas door for a second, and we knowed by that that the rascals had missed their boat and was beginning to understand that they was in just as much trouble now as Jim Turner was.

Then Jim manned the oars and we took out after our raft. Now was the first time that I begun to worry about the men— I reckon I hadn't had time to before. I begun to think how dreadful it was, even for murderers, to be in such a fix. I says to myself, there ain't no telling but I might come to be a murderer myself yet, and then how would I like it? So says I to Jim:

"The first light we see we'll land a hundred yards below it or above it, in a place where it's a good hiding-place for you and the skiff, and then I'll go and fix up some kind of a yarn, and get somebody to go for that gang and get them out of their scrape, so they can be hung when their time comes."

But that idea was a failure, for pretty soon it begun to storm again and this time worse then ever. The rain poured down and never a light showed; everybody in bed, I reckon. We boomed along down the river, watching for lights and watching for our raft. After a long time the rain let up but the clouds stayed, and the lightning kept whimpering and by and by a flash showed us a black thing ahead, floating, and we made for it.

It was the raft, and mighty glad was we to get aboard of it again. We seen a light now away down to the right, on shore. So I said I would go for it. The skiff was half full of plunder which that gang had stole there on the wreck. We hustled it onto the raft in a pile, and I told Jim to float along down, and show a light when he judged he had gone about two mile and keep it burning till I come; then I manned my oars and shoved for the light. As I got down towards it three or four more showed—upon a hillside. It was a village. I closed in above the shore light, and laid on my oars and floated. As I went by I see it was a lantern hanging on the jack-staff of a double-hull ferryboat. I skimmed around for the watchman, a-wondering whereabouts he slept; and by and by I found him roosting on the bitts forward, with his head down between his knees. I give his shoulder two or three little shoves, and begun to cry.

He stirred up in a kind of startlish way, but when he see it was only me he took a good gap and stretch, and then he says:

"Hello, what's up? Don't cry, bub. What's the trouble?"

I says:

"Pap, and mam, and sis, and—"

Then I broke down. He says:

"Oh, dang it now, *don't* take on so; we all has to have our troubles, and this'n 'll come out all right. What's the matter with 'em?"

"They're—they're—are you the watchman of the boat?"

"Yes," he says, kind of pretty-well-satisfied like. "I'm the captain and the owner and the mate and the pilot and watchman and head deck-hand, and sometimes I'm the freight and passengers. I ain't as rich as old Jim Hornback, and I can't be so blame' generous and good to Tom, Dick, and Harry as what he is and slam around money the way he does, but I've told him a many a time 't I wouldn't trade places with him; for, says I, a sailor's life's the life for me and I'm derned if *I'd* live two mile out o' town, where there ain't nothing ever goin' on, not for all his spondulicks and as much more on top of it. Says I—"

I broke in and says:

"They're in an awful peck of trouble, and———"

"*Who* is?"

"Why, pap and mam and sis and Miss Hooker, and if you'd take your ferryboat and go up there—"

"Up where? Where are they?"

"On the wreck."

"What wreck?"

"Why, there ain't but one."

"What, you don't mean the *Walter Scott?*"

"Yes."

"Good land! what are they doin' *there,* for gracious sakes?"

"Well, they didn't go there a-purpose."

"I bet they didn't! Why, great goodness, there ain't no chance for 'em if they don't git off mighty quick! Why, how in the nation did they ever git into such a scrape?"

"Easy enough. Miss Hooker was a-visiting up there to the town——"

"Yes, Booth's Landing—go on."

"She was a-visiting there at Booth's Landing, and just in the edge of the evening she started over with her nigger woman in the horse-ferry to stay all night at her friend's house, Miss What-you-may-call-her—I disremember her name—and they lost their steering-oar and the ferryman and the nigger woman and the horses was swung around and went a-floating down, stern first, about two mile, and saddle-baggsed on the wreck, and all lost, but Miss Hooker she made a grab and got aboard the wreck. Well, about an hour after dark we come along down in our trading-scow, and it was so dark we didn't notice the wreck till we was right on it; and so *we* saddle-baggsed, but all of us was saved but Bill Whipple—and oh, he *was* the best cretur!—I most wisht it had been me, I do."

"My George! It's the beatenest thing I ever struck. And *then* what did you all do?"

"Well, we hollered and took on but it's so wide there we couldn't make nobody hear. So pap said somebody got to get ashore and get help somehow. I was the only one that could swim, so I made a dash for it, and Miss Hooker she said if I didn't strike help sooner, come here and hunt up her uncle, and he'd fix the thing. I made the land about a mile below, and been fooling along ever since, trying to get people to do something, but they said, 'What, in such a night and such a current? There ain't no sense in it; go for the steam-ferry.' Now if you'll go and——"

"By Jackson, I'd *like* to, and, blame it, I don't know but I will; but who in the dingnation's a-going to *pay* for it? Do you reckon your pap——"

"Why *that's* all right. Miss Hooker she told me, *particular,* that her uncle Hornback——"

259

"Great guns; is *he* her uncle? Looky here, you break for that light over yonder-way, and turn out west when you git there, and about a quarter of a mile out you'll come to the tavern; tell 'em to dart you out to Jim Hornback's and he'll foot the bill. And don't you fool around any, because he'll want to know the news. Tell him I'll have his niece all safe before he can get to town. Hump yourself, now; I'm a-going up around the corner here to roust out my engineer."

I struck for the light, but as soon as he turned the corner I went back and got into my skiff and bailed her out, and then pulled up shore in the easy water about six hundred yards and tucked myself in among some wood-boats; for I couldn't rest easy till I could see the ferryboat start. But take it all around, I was feeling ruther comfortable on accounts of taking all this trouble for that gang, for not many would 'a' done it. I wished the widow knowed about it. I judged she would be proud of me for helping these rapscallions, because rapscallions and deadbeats is the kind the widow and good people takes the most interest in.

Well, before long here comes the wreck, dim and dusky, sliding along down! A kind of cold shiver went through me, and then I struck out for her. She was very deep and I see in a minute there warn't much chance of anybody being alive in her. I pulled all around her and hollered a little, but there wasn't any answer; all dead still. I felt a little bit heavy-hearted about the gang but not much, for I reckoned if they could stand it I could.

Then here comes the ferryboat; so I shoved for the middle of the river on a long downstream slant; and when I judged I was out of eye-reach I laid on my oars, and looked back and see her go and smell around the wreck for Miss Hooker's remainders, because the captain would know her uncle Hornback would want them, and then pretty soon the ferryboat give it up and went for the shore and I laid into my work and went a-booming down the river.

It did seem a powerful long time before Jim's light showed up, and when it did show it looked like it was a thousand mile off. By the time I got there the sky was beginning to get a little gray in the east; so we struck for an island and hid the raft and sunk the skiff, and turned in and slept like dead people.

Adventures of Huckleberry Finn

Mark Twain

CHAPTER 14

WAS SOLOMON WISE?

By and by, when we got up, we turned over the truck the gang had stole off of the wreck, and found boots and blankets and clothes and all sorts of other things, and a lot of books and a spy-glass and three boxes of seegars. We hadn't ever been this rich before in neither of our lives. The seegars was prime. We laid off all the afternoon in the woods talking, and me reading the books, and having a general good time. I told Jim all about what happened inside the wreck and at the ferryboat and I said these kinds of things was adventures, but he said he didn't want no more adventures. He said that when I went in the texas and he crawled back to get on the raft and found her gone he nearly died, because he judged it was all up with *him* anyway it could be fixed, for if he didn't get saved he would get drownded, and if he did get saved, whoever saved him would send him back home so as to get the reward, and then Miss Watson would sell him South, sure. Well, he was right; he was most always right; he had an uncommon level head for a nigger.

I read considerable to Jim about kings and dukes and earls and such, and how gaudy they dressed and how much style they put on, and called each other your majesty, and your grace, and your lordship, and so on, 'stead of mister, and Jim's eyes bugged out and he was interested. He says:

"I didn' know dey was so many un um. I hain't hearn 'bout none un um, skasely, but ole King Sollermun, onless you counts dem kings dat's in a pack er k'yards. How much do a king git?"

"Get?" I says, "why, they get a thousand dollars a month if they want it; they can have just as much as they want; everything belongs to them."

"Ain' dat gay? En what dey got to do, Huck?"

"They don't do nothing! Why, how you talk. They just set around."

"No; is dat so?"

"Of course it is. They just set around—except, maybe, when there's a war; then they go to the war. But other times they just lazy around, or go hawking—just hawking and sp— Sh!—d'you hear a noise?"

We skipped out and looked; but it warn't nothing but the flutter of a steamboat's wheel away down, coming around the point; so we come back.

"Yes," says I, "and other times, when things is dull, they fuss with the parlyment, and if everybody don't go just so he whacks their heads off. But mostly they hang 'round the harem."

" 'Roun' de which?"

"Harem."

"What's de harem?"

"The place where he keeps his wives. Don't you know about the harem? Solomon had one; he had about a million wives."

"Why, yes, dat's so; I—I'd done forgot it. A harem's a bo'd'n-house, I reck'n. Mos' likely dey has rackety times in de nussery. En I reck'n de wives quarrels considable, en dat 'crease de racket. Yet dey say Sollermun de wises' man dat ever live'. I doan' take no stock in dat. Bekase why: would a wise man want to live in de mids' er sich a blimblammin' all de time? No—'deed he wouldn't. A wise man 'ud take en buil' a biler-factry, en den he could shet *down* de biler-factry when he want to res'."

"Well, but he *was* the wisest man, anyway, because the widow she told me so, her own self."

"I doan' k'yer what de widder say, he *warn't* no wise man nuther. He had some er de dad-fetchedes' ways I ever see. Does you know 'bout dat chile dat he 'uz gwyne to chop in two?"

"Yes, the widow told me all about it."

"*Well,* den! Warn' dat de beatenes' notion in de worl'? You jes' take en look at it a minute. Dah's de stump, dah— dat's one er de women; heah's you—dat's de yuther one; I's Sollermun; en dish yer dollar bill's de chile. Bofe un you claims it. What does I do? Does I shin aroun' mongs' de neighbors en fine out which un you de bill *do* b'long to, en 'han' it over to de right one, all safe en soun', de way dat anybody dat had any gumption would? No; I take en whack de bill in *two,* en give half un it to you, en de yuther half to de yuther woman. Dat's de way Sollermun was gwyne to do wid de chile. Now I want to ast you: what's de use er dat half a bill?—can't buy noth'n' wid it. En what use is a half a chile? I wouldn' give a dern for a million un um."

"But hang it, Jim, you've clean missed the point—blame it, you've missed it a thousand mile."

"Who? Me? Go 'long. Doan' talk to *me* 'bout yo' p'ints. I reck'n I knows sense when I sees it; en dey ain' no sense in sich doin's as dat. De 'spute warn't 'bout a half a chile, de 'spute was 'bout a whole chile, en de man dat think he kin settle a 'spute 'bout a whole chile wid a half a chile doan' know enough to come in out'n de rain. Doan' talk to me 'bout Sollermun, Huck, I knows him by de back."

"But I tell you you don't get the point."

"Blame de p'int! I reck'n I knows what I knows. En mine you, de *real* p'int is down furder—it's down deeper. It lays in de way Sollermun was raised. You take a man dat's got on'y one er two chillen; is dat man gwyne to be waseful o' chillen? No, he ain't; he can't 'ford it. *He* know how to value 'em. But you take a man dat's got 'bout five million chillen runnin' roun' de house, en it's diffunt. *He* as soon chop a chile in two as a cat. Dey's plenty mo'. A chile er two, mo' er less, warn't no consekens to Sollermun, dad fetch him!"

I never see such a nigger. If he got a notion in his head once, there warn't no getting it out again. He was the most down on Solomon of any nigger I ever see. So I went to talking about other kings, and let Solomon slide. I told about Louis Sixteenth that got his head cut off in France long time ago; and about his little boy the dolphin, that would 'a' been a king, but they took and shut him up in jail and some say he died there.

"Po' little chap."

"But some says he got out and got away, and come to America."

"Dat's good! But he'll be pooty lonesome—dey ain' no kings here, is dey, Huck?"

"No."

"Den he cain't git no situation. What he gwyne to do?"

"Well, I don't know. Some of them gets on the police, and some of them learns people how to talk French."

265

"Why, Huck, doan' de French people talk de same way we does?"

"*No*, Jim; you couldn't understand a word they said—not a single word."

"Well, now, I be ding-busted! How do dat come?"

"*I* don't know; but it's so. I got some of their jabber out of a book. S'pose a man was to come to you and say Polly-voo-franzy—what would you think?"

"I wouldn' think nuffn; I'd take en bust him over de head—dat is, ef he warn't white. I wouldn't 'low no nigger to call me dat."

"Shucks, it ain't calling you anything. It's only saying, do you know how to talk French?"

"Well, den, why couldn't he say it?"

"Why, he *is* a-saying it. That's a Frenchman's *way* of saying it."

"Well, it's a blame' ridicklous way, en I doan' want to hear no mo' 'bout it. Dey ain' no sense in it."

"Looky here, Jim; does a cat talk like we do?"

"No, a cat don't."

"Well, does a cow?"

"No, a cow don't, nuther."

"Does a cat talk like a cow, or a cow talk like a cat?"

"No, dey don't."

"It's natural and right for 'em to talk different from each other, ain't it?"

"Course."

"And ain't it natural and right for a cat and a cow to talk different from *us*?"

"Why, mos' sholy it is."

"Well, then, why ain't it natural and right for a *Frenchman* to talk different from us? You answer me that."

"Is a cat a man, Huck?"

"No."

"Well, den, dey ain't no sense in a cat talkin' like a man. Is a cow a man?—er is a cow a cat?"

"No, she ain't either of them."

"Well, den, she ain' got no business to talk like either one er the yuther of 'em. Is a Frenchman a man?"

"Yes."

"*Well,* den! Dad blame it, why doan' he *talk* like a man? You answer me *dat!*"

I see it warn't no use wasting words—you can't learn a nigger to argue. So I quit.

CHAPTER 15

FOOLING POOR OLD JIM

We judged that three nights more would fetch us to Cairo, at the bottom of Illinois, where the Ohio River comes in, and that was what we was after. We would sell the raft and get on a steamboat and go way up the Ohio amongst the free states, and then be out of trouble.

Well, the second night a fog begun to come on and we made for a towhead to tie to, for it wouldn't do to try to run in a fog, but when I paddled ahead in the canoe with the line to make fast, there warn't anything but little saplings to tie to. I passed the line around one of them right on the edge of the cut bank, but there was a stiff current and the raft come booming down so lively she tore it out by the roots and away she went. I see the fog closing down, and it made me so sick and scared I couldn't budge for most a half a minute it seemed to me—and then there warn't no raft in sight; you couldn't see twenty yards. I jumped into the canoe and run back to the stern and grabbed the paddle and set her back a stroke. But she didn't come. I was in such a hurry I hadn't untied her. I got up and tried to untie her, but I was so excited my hands shook so I couldn't hardly do anything with them.

As soon as I got started I took out after the raft, hot and heavy, right down the towhead. That was all right as far as it went but the towhead warn't sixty yards long, and the minute I flew by the foot of it I shot out into the solid white fog and hadn't no more idea which way I was going than a dead man.

Thinks I, it won't do to paddle, first I know I'll run into the bank or a towhead or something, I got to set still and float and yet it's mighty fidgety business to have to hold your hands still at such a time. I whooped and listened. Away down there somewheres I hears a small whoop and up comes my spirits. I went tearing after it, listening sharp to hear it again. The next time it come I see I warn't heading for it, but heading away to the right of it. And the next time I was heading away to the left of it—and not gaining on it much either, for I was flying around, this way and that and t'other, but it was going straight ahead all the time.

I did wish the fool would think to beat a tin pan, and beat it all the time but he never did, and it was the still places between the whoops that was making the trouble for me. Well, I fought along, and directly I hears the whoop *behind* me. I was tangled good now. That was somebody else's whoop, or else I was turned around.

I throwed the paddle down. I heard the whoop again; it was behind me yet but in a different place; it kept coming and kept changing its place and I kept answering, till by and by it was in front of me again and I knowed the current had swung the canoe's head downstream and I was all right if that was Jim and not some other raftsman hollering. I couldn't tell nothing about voices in a fog, for nothing don't look natural nor sound natural in a fog.

The whooping went on and in about a minute I come a-booming down on a cut bank with smoky ghosts of big trees on it, and the current throwed me off to the left and shot by amongst a lot of snags that fairly roared, the current was tearing by them so swift.

In another second or two it was solid white and still again. I set perfectly still then, listening to my heart thump, and I reckon I didn't draw a breath while it thumped a hundred.

I just give up then. I knowed what the matter was. That cut bank was an island and Jim had gone down t'other side of it. It warn't no towhead that you could float by in ten minutes. It had the big timber of a regular island; it might be five or six mile long and more than half a mile wide.

I kept quiet, with my ears cocked, about fifteen minutes, I reckon. I was floating along, of course, four or five mile an hour, but you don't ever think of that. No, you *feel* like you are laying dead still on the water, and if a little glimpse of a snag slips by you don't think to yourself how fast *you're* going, but you catch your breath and think, my! how that snag's tearing along. If you think it ain't dismal and lonesome out in a fog that way by yourself in the night, you try it once—you'll see.

Next, for about a half an hour, I whoops now and then; at last I hears the answer a long ways off, and tries to follow it but I couldn't do it, and directly I judged I'd got into a nest of towheads, for I had little dim glimpses of them on both sides of me—sometimes just a narrow channel between, and some that I couldn't see I knowed was there because I'd hear the wash of the current against the old dead brush and trash that hung over the banks. Well, I warn't long losing the whoops down amongst the towheads, and I only tried to chase them a little while, anyway, because it was worse than chasing a Jack-o-lantern. You never knowed a sound dodge around so and swap places so quick and so much.

I had to claw away from the bank pretty lively four or five times, to keep from knocking the islands out of the river, and so I judged the raft must be butting into the bank every now and then or else it would get further ahead and clear out of hearing—it was floating a little faster than what I was.

Well, I seemed to be in the open river again by and by, but I couldn't hear no sign of a whoop nowheres. I reckoned Jim had fetched up on a snag, maybe, and it was all up with him. I was good and tired, so I laid down in the canoe and said I wouldn't bother no more. I didn't want to go to sleep, of course; but I was so sleepy I couldn't help it; so I thought I would take jest one little cat-nap.

But I reckon it was more than a cat-nap, for when I waked up the stars was shining bright, the fog was all gone, and I was spinning down a big bend stern first. First I didn't know where I was; I thought I was dreaming; and when things begun to come back to me they seemed to come up dim out of last week.

It was a monstrous big river here, with the tallest and the thickest kind of timber on both banks, just a solid wall, as well as I could see by the stars. I looked away downstream and seen a black speck on the water. I took out after it, but when I got to it it warn't nothing but a couple of saw-logs made fast together. Then I see another speck and chased that; then another, and this time I was right. It was the raft.

When I got to it Jim was setting there with his head down between his knees, asleep, with his right arm hanging over the steering-oar. The other oar was smashed off and the raft was littered up with leaves and branches and dirt. So she'd had a rough time.

I made fast and laid down under Jim's nose on the raft, and begun to gap and stretch my fists out against Jim, and says:

"Hello, Jim, have I been asleep? Why didn't you stir me up?"

"Goodness gracious, is dat you, Huck? En you ain' dead—you ain' drownded—you's back agin? It's too good for true, honey, it's too good for true. Lemme look at you, chile, lemme feel o' you. No, you ain' dead! you's back agin, 'live en soun', jis' de same ole Huck—de same ole Huck, thanks to goodness!"

"What's the matter with you, Jim? You been a-drinking?"

"Drinkin'? Has I ben a-drinkin'? Has I had a chance to be a-drinkin'?"

"Well, then, what makes you talk so wild?"

"How does I talk wild?"

"*How?* Why, hain't you been talking about my coming back, and all that stuff, as if I'd been gone away?"

"Huck—Huck Finn, you look me in de eye; look me in de eye. *Hain't* you ben gone away?"

"Gone away? Why, what in the nation do you mean? I hain't been gone anywheres. Where would I go to?"

"Well, looky here, boss, dey's sumfn wrong, dey is. Is I *me,* or who *is* I? Is I heah, or whah *is* I? Now dat's what I wants to know."

"Well, I think you're here, plain enough, but I think you're a tangle-headed old fool, Jim."

"I is, is I? Well, you answer me dis: Didn't you tote out de line in de canoe fer to make fas' to de towhead?"

"No, I didn't. What towhead? I hain't seen no towhead."

"You hain't seen no towhead? Looky here, didn't de line pull loose en de raf' go a-hummin' down de river, en leave you en de canoe behine in de fog?"

"What fog?"

"Why, *de* fog!—de fog dat's ben aroun' all night. En didn't you whoop, en didn't I whoop, tell we got mix' up in de islands en one un us got los' en t'other one was jis' as good as los', 'kase he didn't know whah he wuz? En didn't I bust up

271

agin a lot er dem islands en have a turrible time en mos' git drownded? Now ain' dat so, boss—ain't it so? You answer me dat."

"Well, this is too many for me, Jim. I hain't seen no fog, nor no islands, nor no troubles, nor nothing. I been setting here talking with you all night till you went to sleep about ten minutes ago, and I reckon I done the same. You couldn't 'a' got drunk in that time, so of course you've been dreaming."

"Dad fetch it, how is I gwyne to dream all dat in ten minutes?"

"Well, hang it all, you did dream it, because there didn't any of it happen."

"But, Huck, it's all jis' as plain to me as—"

"It don't make no difference how plain it is; there ain't nothing in it. I know, because I've been here all the time."

Jim didn't say nothing for about five minutes, but set there studying over it. Then he says:

"Well, den, I reck'n I did dream it, Huck; but dog my cats ef it ain't de powerfulest dream I ever see. En I hain't ever had no dream b'fo' dat's tired me like dis one."

"Oh, well, that's all right, because a dream does tire a body like everything sometimes. But this one was a staving dream; tell me all about it, Jim."

So Jim went to work and told me the whole thing right through, just as it happened, only he painted it up considerable. Then he said he must start in and " 'terpret" it, because it was sent for a warning. He said the first towhead stood for a man that would try to do us some good, but the current was another man that would get us away from him. The whoops was warnings that would come to us every now and then, and if we didn't try hard to make out to understand them they'd just take us into bad luck, 'stead of keeping us out of it. The lot of towheads was troubles we was going to get into with quarrelsome people and all kinds of mean folks, but if we minded our business and didn't talk back and aggravate them, we would pull through and get out of the fog and into the big clear river, which was the free states, and wouldn't have no more trouble.

It had clouded up pretty dark just after I got on to the raft, but it was clearing up again now.

"Oh, well, that's all interpreted well enough as far as it goes, Jim," I says; "but what does *these* things stand for?"

It was the leaves and rubbish on the raft and the smashed oar. You could see them first-rate now.

Jim looked at the trash, and then looked at me, and back at the trash again. He had got the dream fixed so strong in his head that he couldn't seem to shake it loose and get the facts back into its place again right away. But when he did get the thing straightened around he looked at me steady without ever smiling, and says:

"What do dey stan' for? I's gwyne to tell you. When I got all wore out wid work, en wid de callin' for you, en went to sleep, my heart wuz mos' broke bekase you wuz los', en I didn' k'yer no mo' what become er me en de raf'. En when I wake up en fine you back agin, all safe en soun', de tears come, en I could 'a' got down on my knees en kiss yo' foot, I's so thankful. En all you wuz thinkin' 'bout wuz how you could make a fool uv ole Jim wid a lie. Dat truck dah is *trash;* en trash is what people is dat puts dirt on de head er dey fren's en makes 'em ashamed."

Then he got up slow and walked to the wigwam, and went in there without saying anything but that. But that was enough. It made me feel so mean I could almost kissed *his* foot to get him to take it back.

It was fifteen minutes before I could work myself up to go and humble myself to a nigger—but I done it and I warn't

273

ever sorry for it afterward, neither. I didn't do him no more mean tricks, and I wouldn't done that one if I'd 'a' knowed it would make him feel that way.

CHAPTER 16

THE RATTLESNAKE-SKIN DOES ITS WORK

We slept most all day, and started out at night, a little ways behind a monstrous long raft that was as long going by as a procession. She had four long sweeps at each end, so we judged she carried as many as thirty men, likely. She had five big wigwams aboard, wide apart, and an open campfire in the middle and a tall flag-pole at each end. There was a power of style about her. It *amounted* to something being a raftsman on such a craft as that.

We went drifting down into a big bend and the night clouded up and got hot. The river was very wide and was walled with solid timber on both sides; you couldn't see a break in it hardly ever, or a light. We talked about Cairo and wondered whether we would know it when we got to it. I said likely we wouldn't, because I had heard say there warn't but about a dozen houses there and if they didn't happen to have them lit up, how was we going to know we was passing a town? Jim said if the two big rivers joined together there, that would show. But I said maybe we might think we was passing the foot of an island and coming into the same old river again. That disturbed Jim—and me too. So the question was, what to do? I said, paddle ashore the first time a light showed and tell them pap was behind, coming along with a trading-scow, and was a green hand at the business and want-ed to know how far it was to Cairo. Jim thought it was a good idea, so we took a smoke on it and waited.

There warn't nothing to do now but to look out sharp for the town and not pass it without seeing it. He said he'd be mighty sure to see it because he'd be a free man the minute he seen it, but if he missed it he'd be in a slave country again and no more show for freedom. Every little while he jumps up and says:

"Dah she is!"

But it warn't. It was Jack-o-lanterns or lightning-bugs, so he set down again and went to watching, same as before. Jim said it made him all over trembly and feverish to be so close to freedom. Well, I can tell you it made me all over trembly and feverish, too, to hear him, because I begun to get it through my head that he *was* most free—and who was to blame for it? Why, *me*. I couldn't get that out of my conscience, no how nor no way. It got to troubling me so I couldn't rest; I couldn't stay still in one place. It hadn't ever come home to me before, what this thing was that I was doing. But now it did, and it stayed with me and scorched me more and more. I tried to make out to myself that *I* warn't to blame because *I* didn't run Jim off from his rightful owner, but it warn't no use, conscience up and says, every time, "But you knowed he was running for his freedom, and you could 'a' paddled ashore and told some-body." That was so—I couldn't get around that no way. That was where it pinched. Conscience says to me, "What had poor Miss Watson done to you that you could see her nigger go off right under your eyes and never say one single word? What did that poor old woman do to you that you could treat her so mean? Why, she tried to learn you your book, she tried to learn you your manners, she tried to be good to you every way she knowed how. *That's* what she done."

I got to feeling so mean and so miserable I most wished I was dead. I fidgeted up and down the raft, abusing myself to myself, and Jim was fidgeting up and down past me. We

275

neither of us could keep still. Every time he danced around and says, "Dah's Cairo!" it went through me like a shot, and I thought if it *was* Cairo I reckoned I would die of miserableness.

Jim talked out loud all the time while I was talking to myself. He was saying how the first thing he would do when he got to a free state he would go to saving up money and never spend a single cent, and when he got enough he would buy his wife, which was owned on a farm close to where Miss Watson lived, and then they would both work to buy the two children, and if their master wouldn't sell them, they'd get an Ab'litionist to go and steal them.

It most froze me to hear such talk. He wouldn't ever dared to talk such talk in his life before. Just see what a difference it made in him the minute he judged he was about free. It was according to the old saying, "Give a nigger an inch and he'll take an ell." Thinks I, this is what comes of my not thinking. Here was this nigger, which I had as good as helped to run away, coming right out flat-footed and saying he would steal his children—children that belonged to a man I didn't even know; a man that hadn't ever done me no harm.

I was sorry to hear Jim say that, it was such a lowering of him. My conscience got to stirring me up hotter than ever, until at last I says to it, "Let up on me—it ain't too late yet— I'll paddle ashore at the first light and tell." I felt easy and happy and light as a feather right off. All my troubles was gone. I went to looking out sharp for a light, and sort of singing to myself. By and by one showed. Jim sings out:

"We's safe, Huck, we's safe! Jump up and crack yo' heels! Dat's de good ole Cairo at las', I jis' knows it!"

I says:

"I'll take the canoe and go see, Jim. It mightn't be, you know."

He jumped and got the canoe ready and put his old coat in the bottom for me to set on and give me the paddle; and as I shoved off, he says:

"Pooty soon I'll be a-shout'n' for joy, en I'll say, it's all on accounts o' Huck; I's a free man, en I couldn't ever ben free ef it hadn' ben for Huck; Huck done it. Jim won't ever forget you, Huck; you's de bes' fren' Jim's ever had; en you's de *only* fren' ole Jim's got now."

I was paddling off, all in a sweat to tell on him, but when he says this, it seemed to kind of take the tuck all out of me. I went along slow then, and I warn't right down certain whether I was glad I started or whether I warn't. When I was fifty yards off, Jim says:

"Dah you goes, de ole true Huck; de on'y white genleman dat ever kep' his promise to ole Jim."

Well, I just felt sick. But I says, I *got* to do it—I can't get *out* of it. Right then along comes a skiff with two men in it with guns, and they stopped and I stopped. One of them says:

"What's that yonder?"

"A piece of a raft," I says.

"Do you belong on it?"

"Yes, sir."

"Any men on it?"

"Only one, sir."

"Well, there's five niggers run off tonight up yonder, above the head of the bend. Is your man white or black?"

I didn't answer up prompt. I tried to, but the words wouldn't come. I tried for a second or two to brace up and out with it, but I warn't man enough—hadn't the spunk of a rabbit. I see I was weakening; so I just give up trying, and up and says:

"He's white."

"I reckon we'll go and see for ourselves."

"I wish you would," says I, "because it's pap that's there, and maybe you'd help me tow the raft ashore where the light is. He's sick—and so is mam and Mary Ann."

"Oh, the devil! we're in a hurry, boy. But I s'pose we've got to. Come, buckle to your paddle, and let's get along."

I buckled to my paddle and they laid to their oars. When we had made a stroke or two, I says:

"Pap'll be mighty much obleeged to you, I can tell you. Everybody goes away when I want them to help me tow the raft ashore, and I can't do it by myself."

"Well, that's infernal mean. Odd, too. Say, boy, what's the matter with your father?"

"It's the—a—the—well, it ain't anything much."

They stopped pulling. It warn't but a mighty little ways to the raft now. One says:

"Boy, that's a lie. What *is* the matter with your pap? Answer up square now, and it'll be the better for you."

"I will, sir, I will, honest—but don't leave us, please. It's the—the—Gentlemen, if you'll only pull ahead, and let me heave you the headline, you won't have to come a-near the raft—please do."

"Set her back, John, set her back!" says one. They backed water. "Keep away, boy—keep to looard. Confound it, I just expect the wind has blowed it to us. Your pap's got the small-pox and you know it precious well. Why didn't you come out and say so? Do you want to spread it all over?"

"Well," says I, a-blubbering, "I've told everybody before, and they just went away and left us."

"Poor devil, there's something in that. We are right down sorry for you, but we—well, hang it, we don't want the smallpox, you see. Look here, I'll tell you what to do. Don't you try to land by yourself, or you'll smash everything to pieces. You float along down about twenty miles and you'll come to a town on the left-hand side of the river. It will be long after sun-up then, and when you ask for help you tell them your folks are all down with chills and fever. Don't be a fool again and let people guess what is the matter. Now we're trying to do you a kindness; so you just put twenty miles between us, that's a good boy. It wouldn't do any good to land yonder where the light is—it's only a wood-yard. Say, I reckon your father's poor, and I'm bound to say he's in pretty hard luck. Here, I'll put a twenty-dollar gold piece on this board, and you get it when it floats by. I feel mighty mean to leave you, but my kingdom! it won't do to fool with smallpox, don't you see?"

"Hold on, Parker," says the man, "here's a twenty to put on the board for me. Goodbye, boy; you do as Mr. Parker told you, and you'll be all right."

"That's so, my boy—goodbye, goodbye. If you see any runaway niggers you get help and nab them, and you can make some money by it."

"Goodbye, sir," says I, "I won't let no runaway niggers get by me if I can help it."

They went off and I got aboard the raft, feeling bad and low because I knowed very well I had done wrong, and I see it warn't no use for me to try to learn to do right; a body that don't get *started* right when he's little ain't got no show— when the pinch comes there ain't nothing to back him up and keep him to his work, and so he gets beat. Then I thought a minute and says to myself, hold on; s'pose you'd 'a' done right and give Jim up, would you felt better than what you do now? No, says I, I'd feel bad—I'd feel just the same way I do now. Well, then, says I, what's the use you learning to do right when it's troublesome to do right and ain't no trouble to do wrong, and the wages is just the same? I was stuck. I couldn't answer that. So I reckoned I wouldn't bother no more about

279

it, but after this always do whichever come handiest at the time.

I went into the wigwam; Jim warn't there. I looked all around; he warn't anywhere. I says:

"Jim!"

"Here I is, Huck. Is dey out o' sight yit? Don't talk loud."

He was in the river under the stern oar, with just his nose out. I told him they was out of sight, so he come aboard. He says:

"I was a-listenin' to all de talk, en I slips into de river en was gwyne to shove for sho' if dey come aboard. Den I was gwyne to swim to de raf' agin when dey was gone. But lawsy, how you did fool 'em, Huck! Dat *wuz* de smartes' dodge! I tell you, chile, I 'spec it save' ole Jim—ole Jim ain't gwyne to forgit you for dat, honey."

Then we talked about the money. It was a pretty good raise—twenty dollars apiece. Jim said we could take deck passage on a steamboat now, and the money would last us as far as we wanted to go in the free states. He said twenty mile more warn't far for the raft to go, but he wished we was already there.

Towards daybreak we tied up, and Jim was mighty particular about hiding the raft good. Then he worked all day fixing things in bundles, and getting all ready to quit rafting.

That night about ten we hove in sight of the lights of a town away down in a left-hand bend.

I went off in the canoe to ask about it. Pretty soon I found a man out in the river with a skiff, setting a trot-line. I ranged up and says:

"Mister, is that town Cairo?"

"Cairo? no. You must be a blame' fool."

"What town is it, mister?"

"If you want to know, go and find out. If you stay here botherin' around me for about a half a minute longer you'll get something you won't want."

I paddled to the raft. Jim was awful disappointed, but I said never mind, Cairo would be the next place, I reckoned.

We passed another town before daylight, and I was going out again; but it was high ground, so I didn't go. No high ground about Cairo, Jim said. I had forgot it. We laid up for the day on a towhead tolerable close to the left-hand bank. I begun to suspicion something. So did Jim. I says:

"Maybe we went by Cairo in the fog that night."

He says:

"Doan' le's talk about it, Huck. Po' niggers can't have no luck. I awluz 'spected dat rattlesnake-skin warn't done wid its work."

"I wish I'd never seen that snake-skin, Jim—I do wish I'd never laid eyes on it."

"It ain't yo' fault, Huck; you didn' know. Don't you blame yo'self 'bout it."

When it was daylight, here was the clear Ohio water inshore, sure enough, and outside was the old regular Muddy! So it was all up with Cairo.

We talked it all over. It wouldn't do to take to the shore; we couldn't take the raft up the stream, of course. There warn't no way but to wait for dark and start back in the canoe and take the chances. So we slept all day amongst the cottonwood thicket, so as to be fresh for the work, and when we went back to the raft about dark the canoe was gone!

We didn't say a word for a good while. There warn't anything to say. We both knowed well enough it was some more work of the rattlesnake-skin; so what was the use to talk about it? It would only look like we was finding fault and that would be bound to fetch more bad luck—and keep on fetching it, too, till we knowed enough to keep still.

By and by we talked about what we better do, and found there warn't no way but just to go along down with the raft till we got a chance to buy a canoe to go back in. We warn't going to borrow it when there warn't anybody around, the way pap would do, for that might set people after us.

So we shoved out after dark on the raft.

Anybody that don't believe yet that it's foolishness to handle a snake-skin, after all that that snake-skin done for us, will believe it now if they read on and see what more it done for us.

The place to buy canoes is off of rafts laying up at shore. But we didn't see no rafts laying up; so we went along during three hours and more. Well, the night got gray and ruther thick, which is the next meanest thing to fog. You can't tell the shape of the river and you can't see no distance. It got to be very late and still, and then along comes a steamboat up the river. We lit the lantern and judged she would see it. Upstream boats didn't generly come close to us; they go out and follow the bars and hunt for easy water under the reefs; but nights like this they bull right up the channel against the whole river.

We could hear her pounding along but we didn't see her good till she was close. She aimed right for us. Often they do that and try to see how close they can come without touching; sometimes the wheel bites off a sweep, and then the pilot sticks his head out and laughs and thinks he's mighty smart. Well, here she comes, and we said she was going to try and shave us, but she didn't seem to be sheering off a bit. She was a big one and she was coming in a hurry, too, looking like a black cloud with rows of glow-worms around it, but all of a sudden she bulged out, big and scary, with a long row of wide-open furnace doors shining like red-hot teeth and her monstrous bows and guards hanging right over us. There was a yell at us and a jingling of bells to stop the engines, a pow-wow of cussing, and whistling of steam—and as Jim went overboard on one side and I on the other, she come smashing straight through the raft.

I dived—and I aimed to find the bottom, too, for a thirty-foot wheel had got to go over me, and I wanted it to have plenty of room. I could always stay under water a minute; this time I reckon I stayed under a minute and a half. Then I bounced for the top in a hurry, for I was nearly busting. I popped out to my armpits and blowed the water out of my nose, and puffed a bit. Of course there was a booming cur-rent, and of course that boat started her engines again ten seconds after she stopped them, for they never cared much for raftsmen, so now she was churning along up the river, out of sight in the thick weather, though I could hear her.

I sung out for Jim about a dozen times but I didn't get any answer; so I grabbed a plank that touched me while I was "treading water" and struck out for shore, shoving it ahead of me. But I made out to see that the drift of the current was towards the left-hand shore, which meant that I was in a crossing; so I changed off and went that way.

It was one of these long, slanting, two-mile crossings; so I was a good long time in getting over. I made a safe landing and clumb up the bank. I couldn't see but a little ways but I went poking along over rough ground for a quarter of a mile or more, and then I run across a big old-fashioned double log house before I noticed it. I was going to rush by and get away but a lot of dogs jumped out and went to howling and bark-ing at me, and I knowed better than to move another peg.

CHAPTER 17

THE GRANGERFORDS TAKE ME IN

In about a minute somebody spoke out of a window without putting his head out, and says:

"Be done, boys! Who's there?"

I says:

"It's me."

"Who's me?"

"George Jackson, sir."

"What do you want?"

"I don't want nothing, sir. I only want to go along by, but the dogs won't let me."

"What are you prowling around here this time of night for—hey?"

"I warn't prowling around, sir; I fell overboard off of the steamboat."

"Oh, you did, did you? Strike a light there, somebody. What did you say your name was?"

"George Jackson, sir. I'm only a boy."

"Look here, if you're telling the truth you needn't be afraid—nobody'll hurt you. But don't try to budge; stand right where you are. Rouse out Bob and Tom, some of you, and fetch the guns. George Jackson, is there anybody with you?"

"No, sir, nobody."

I heard the people stirring around in the house now, and see a light. The man sung out:

"Snatch that light away, Betsy, you old fool—ain't you got any sense? Put it on the floor behind the front door. Bob, if you and Tom are ready, take your places."

"All ready."

"Now, George Jackson, do you know the Shepherdsons?"

"No, sir; I never heard of them."

"Well, that may be so, and it mayn't. Now, all ready. Step forward, George Jackson. And mind, don't you hurry—come mighty slow. If there's anybody with you, let him keep back— if he shows himself he'll be shot. Come along now. Come slow; push the door open yourself—just enough to squeeze in, d'you hear?"

I didn't hurry; I couldn't if I'd a-wanted to. I took one slow step at a time and there warn't a sound, only I thought I could hear my heart. The dogs were as still as the humans but they followed a little behind me. When I got to the three log door-steps I heard them unlocking and unbarring and unbolting. I put my hand on the door and pushed it a little and a little more till somebody said, "There, that's enough—put your head in." I done it but I judged they would take it off.

The candle was on the floor and there they all was, looking at me, and me at them, for about a quarter of a minute: three big men with guns pointed at me, which made me wince, I tell you; the oldest gray and about sixty, the other two thirty or more—all of them fine and handsome—and the sweetest old gray-headed lady, and back of her two young women which I couldn't see right well. The old gentleman says:

"There; I reckon it's all right. Come in."

As soon as I was in the old gentleman he locked the door and barred and bolted it, and told the young men to come in with their guns, and they all went in a big parlor that had a new rag carpet on the floor, and got together in a corner that was out of range of the front windows—there warn't none on the side. They held the candle, and took a good look at me, and all said, "Why, *he* ain't a Shepherdson—no, there ain't any Shepherdson about him." Then the old man said he hoped I wouldn't mind being searched for arms, because he didn't mean no harm by it—it was only to make sure. So he didn't pry into my pockets but only felt outside with his hands, and said it was all right. He told me to make myself easy and at home and tell all about myself, but the old lady says:

"Why, bless you, Saul, the poor thing's as wet as he can be, and don't you reckon it may be he's hungry?"

"True for you, Rachel—I forgot."

So the old lady says:

"Betsy" (this was a nigger woman), "you fly around and get him something to eat as quick as you can, poor thing; and one of you girls go and wake up Buck and tell him—oh, here he is himself. Buck, take this little stranger and get the wet clothes off from him and dress him up in some of yours that's dry."

Buck looked about as old as me—thirteen or fourteen or along there, though he was a little bigger than me. He hadn't on anything but a shirt, and he was very frowzy-headed. He came in gaping and digging one fist into his eyes, and he was dragging a gun along with the other one. He says:

"Ain't they no Shepherdsons around?"

They said, no, 'twas a false alarm.

"Well," he says, "if they'd 'a' ben some, I reckon I'd 'a' got one."

They all laughed, and Bob says:

"Why, Buck, they might have scalped us all, you've been so slow in coming."

"Well, nobody come after me, and it ain't right. I'm always kep' down; I don't get no show."

"Never mind, Buck, my boy," says the old man, "you'll have show enough, all in good time, don't you fret about that. Go 'long with you now, and do as your mother told you."

When we got upstairs to his room he got me a coarse shirt and a roundabout and pants of his, and I put them on. While I was at it he asked me what my name was, but before I could tell him he started to tell me about a bluejay and a young rabbit he had catched in the woods day before yesterday, and he asked me where Moses was when the candle went out. I said I didn't know; I hadn't heard about it before, no way.

"Well, guess," he says.

"How'm I going to guess," says I, "when I never heard tell of it before?"

"But you can guess, can't you? It's just as easy."

"*Which* candle?" I says.

"Why, any candle," he says.

"I don't know where he was," says I, "where was he?"

"Why, he was in the *dark*! That's where he was!"

"Well, if you knowed where he was, what did you ask me for?"

"Why, blame it, it's a riddle, don't you see? Say, how long are you going to stay here? You got to stay always. We can just have booming times—they don't have no school now. Do you own a dog? I've got a dog—and he'll go in the river and bring out chips that you throw in. Do you like to comb up Sundays, and all that kind of foolishness? You bet I don't, but ma she makes me. Confound these ole britches! I reckon I'd better put 'em on, but I'd ruther not, it's so warm. Are you all ready? All right. Come along, old hoss."

Cold corn-pone, cold corn-beef, butter and buttermilk—that is what they had for me down there, and there ain't nothing better that ever I've come across yet. Buck and his ma and all of them smoked cob pipes, except the nigger woman, which was gone, and the two young women. They all smoked and talked, and I eat and talked. The young women had quilts around them and their hair down their backs. They all asked me questions, and I told them how pap and me and all the family was living on a little farm down at the bottom of Arkansaw, and my sister Mary Ann run off and got married and never was heard of no more, and Bill went to hunt them and he warn't heard of no more, and Tom and Mort died, and then there warn't nobody but just me and pap left, and he was just trimmed down to nothing, on account of his troubles; so when he died I took what there was left, because the farm didn't belong to us, and started up the river, deck passage, and fell overboard; and that was how I come to be here. So they said I could have a home there as long as I wanted it. Then it was most daylight and everybody went to bed, and I went to bed with Buck, and when I waked up in the morning, drat it all, I had forgot what my name was. So I laid there about an hour trying to think, and when Buck waked up I says:

"Can you spell, Buck?"

"Yes," he says.

"I bet you can't spell my name," says I.

"I bet you what you dare I can," says he.

"All right," says I, "go ahead."

"G-o-r-g-e J-a-x-o-n—there now," he says.

"Well," says I, "you done it, but I didn't think you could. It ain't no slouch of a name to spell—right off without studying."

I set it down, private, because somebody might want *me* to spell it next, and so I wanted to be handy with it and rattle it off like I was used to it.

It was a mighty nice family and a mighty nice house, too. I hadn't seen no house out in the country before that was so nice and had so much style. It didn't have an iron latch on the front door nor a wooden one with a buckskin string, but a brass knob to turn, the same as houses in town. There warn't no bed in the parlor, nor a sign of a bed, but heaps of parlors in towns has beds in them. There was a big fireplace that was bricked on the bottom, and the bricks was kept clean and red by pouring water on them and scrubbing them with another brick; sometimes they wash them over with red water-paint that they call Spanish-brown, same as they do in town. They had big brass dog-irons that could hold up a saw-log. There was a clock on the middle of the mantelpiece, with a picture of a town painted on the bottom half of the glass front, and a round place in the middle of it for the sun, and you could see the pendulum swinging behind it. It was beautiful to hear that clock tick, and sometimes when one of these peddlers had been along and scoured her up and got her in good shape, she would start in and strike a hundred and fifty before she got tuckered out. They wouldn't took any money for her.

Well, there was a big outlandish parrot on each side of the clock, made out of something like chalk and painted up gaudy. By one of the parrots was a cat made of crockery, and a crockery dog by the other; and when you pressed down on them they squeaked but didn't open their mouths nor look different nor interested. They squeaked through underneath. There was a couple of big wild-turkey-wing fans spread out behind those things. On the table in the middle of the room was a kind of a lovely crockery basket that had apples and oranges and peaches and grapes piled up in it, which was much redder and yellower and prettier than real ones is, but they warn't real because you could see where pieces had got chipped off and showed the white chalk, or whatever it was, underneath.

This table had a cover made out of beautiful oilcloth, with a red and blue spread-eagle painted on it and a painted border all around. It come all the way from Philadelphia, they said. There was some books, too, piled up perfectly exact, on each corner of the table. One was a big family Bible full of pictures. One was *Pilgrim's Progress,* about a man that left his family, it didn't say why. I read considerable in it now and then. The statements was interesting but tough. Another was *Friendship's*

Offering, full of beautiful stuff and poetry, but I didn't read the poetry. Another was Henry Clay's *Speeches,* and another was Dr. Gunn's *Family Medicine,* which told you all about what to do if a body was sick or dead. There was a hymn-book and a lot of other books. And there was nice split-bottom chairs, and perfectly sound, too—not bagged down in the middle and busted, like an old basket.

They had pictures hung on the walls—mainly Washingtons and Lafayettes, and battles, and Highland Marys, and one called "Signing the Declaration." There was some that they called crayons, which one of the daughters which was dead made her own self when she was only fifteen years old. They was different from any pictures I ever see before—blacker, mostly, than is common. One was a woman in a slim black dress, belted small under the armpits, with bulges like a cabbage in the middle of the sleeves, and a large black scoop-shovel bonnet with a black veil, and white slim ankles crossed about with black tape and very wee black slippers, like a chisel, and she was leaning pensive on a tombstone on her right elbow under a weeping willow, and her other hand hanging down her side holding a white handkerchief and a reticule, and underneath the picture it said "Shall I Never See Thee More Alas." Another one was a young lady with her hair all combed up straight to the top of her head and knotted there in front of a comb like a chair-back, and she was crying into a handkerchief and had a dead bird laying on its back in her other hand with its heels up, and underneath the picture it said "I Shall Never Hear Thy Sweet Chirrup More Alas." There was one where a young lady was at a window looking up at the moon, and tears running down her cheeks; and she had an open letter in one hand with black sealing wax showing on one edge of it, and she was mashing a locket with a chain to it against her mouth and underneath the picture it

said "And Art Thou Gone Yes Thou Art Gone Alas." These
was all nice pictures, I reckon, but I didn't somehow seem to
take to them, because if ever I was down a little they always
give me the fantods. Everybody was sorry she died, because
she had laid out a lot more of these pictures to do and a body
could see by what she had done what they had lost. But I
reckoned that with her disposition she was having a better
time in the graveyard. She was at work on what they said was
her greatest picture when she took sick, and every day and
every night it was her prayer to be allowed to live till she got
it done, but she never got the chance. It was a picture of a
young woman in a long white gown, standing on the rail of a
bridge all ready to jump off, with her hair all down her back,
and looking up to the moon with the tears running down
her face, and she had two arms folded across her breast and
two arms stretched out in front and two more reaching up
towards the moon—and the idea was to see which pair would
look best and then scratch out all the other arms; but, as I
was saying, she died before she got her mind made up and
now they kept this picture over the head of the bed in her
room, and every time her birthday come they hung flowers
on it. Other times it was hid with a little curtain. The young
woman in the picture had a kind of a nice sweet face but there
was so many arms it made her look too spidery, seemed to me.

This young girl kept a scrapbook when she was alive, and
used to paste obituaries and accidents and cases of patient
suffering in it out of the *Presbyterian Observer,* and write
poetry after them out of her own head. It was very good
poetry. This is what she wrote about a boy by the name of
Stephen Dowling Bots that fell down a well and was
drownded:

And did young Stephen sicken,
   And did young Stephen die?
And did the sad hearts thicken,
   And did the mourners cry?

No; such was not the fate of
   Young Stephen Dowling Bots;
Though sad hearts round him thickened,
   'Twas not from sickness' shots.

No whooping-cough did rack his frame,
   Nor measles drear with spots;
Not these impaired the sacred name
   Of Stephen Dowling Bots.

Despised love struck not with woe
   That head of curly knots,
Nor stomach troubles laid him low,
   Young Stephen Dowling Bots.

O no. Then list with tearful eye,
   Whilst I his fate do tell.
His soul did from this cold world fly
   By falling down a well.

They got him out and emptied him;
   Alas it was too late;
His spirit was gone for to sport aloft
   In the realms of the good and great.

If Emmeline Grangerford could make poetry like that before she was fourteen, there ain't no telling what she could 'a' done by and by. Buck said she could rattle off poetry like nothing. She didn't ever have to stop to think. He said she would slap down a line, and if she couldn't find anything to rhyme with it she would just scratch it out and slap down another one and go ahead. She warn't particular; she could write about anything you choose to give her to write about just so it was sadful. Every time a man died or a woman died or a child died, she would be on hand with her "tribute" before he was cold. She called them tributes. The neighbors said it was the doctor first, then Emmeline, then the undertaker—the undertaker never got in ahead of Emmeline but once, and then she hung fire on a rhyme for the dead person's name, which was Whistler. She warn't ever the same after that; she never complained but she kind of pined away and did not live long. Poor thing, many's the time I made myself go up to the little room that used to be hers and get out her poor old scrapbook and read in it when her pictures had been aggravating me and I had soured on her a little. I liked all that family, dead ones and all, and warn't going to let anything come between us. Poor Emmeline made poetry about all the dead people when she was alive, and it didn't seem right that there warn't nobody to make some about her now she was gone; so I tried to sweat out a verse or two myself but I couldn't seem to make it go somehow. They kept Emmeline's room trim and nice, and all the things fixed in it just the way she liked to have them when she was alive, and nobody ever slept there. The old lady took care of the room herself, though there was plenty of niggers, and she sewed there a good deal and read her Bible there mostly.

Well, as I was saying about the parlor, there was beautiful curtains on the windows: white, with pictures painted on them of castles with vines all down the walls and cattle coming down to drink. There was a little old piano, too, that had tin pans in it, I reckon, and nothing was ever so lovely as to hear the young ladies sing "The Last Link Is Broken" and play "The Battle of Prague" on it. The walls of all the rooms was plastered and most had carpets on the floors, and the whole house was whitewashed on the outside.

It was a double house and the big open place betwixt them was roofed and floored, and sometimes the table was set there in the middle of the day, and it was a cool, comfortable place. Nothing couldn't be better. And warn't the cooking good, and just bushels of it too!

CHAPTER 18

WHY HARNEY RODE AWAY FOR HIS HAT

Col. Grangerford was a gentleman, you see. He was a gentleman all over, and so was his family. He was well born, as the saying is, and that's worth as much in a man as it is in a horse, so the Widow Douglas said, and nobody ever denied that she was of the first aristocracy in our town; and pap he always said it, too, though he warn't no more quality than a mudcat himself. Col. Grangerford was very tall and very slim, and had a darkish-paly complexion, not a sign of red in it anywheres; he was clean-shaved every morning all over his thin face, and he had the thinnest kind of lips and the thinnest kind of nostrils, and a high nose and heavy eyebrows, and the blackest kind of eyes, sunk so deep back that they seemed like they was looking out of caverns at you, as you may say. His forehead was high and his hair was gray and straight and hung to his shoulders. His hands was long and thin, and every day of his life he put on a clean shirt and a full suit from head to foot made out of linen so white it hurt your eyes to look at it, and on Sundays he wore a blue tail-coat with brass buttons on it. He carried a mahogany cane with a silver head to it. There warn't no frivolishness about him, not a bit, and he warn't ever loud. He was as kind as he could be—you could feel that, you know, and so you had confidence. Sometimes he smiled and it was good to see, but when he straightened

himself up like a liberty pole and the lightning begun to
flicker out from under his eyebrows, you wanted to climb a
tree first and find out what the matter was afterwards. He
didn't ever have to tell anybody to mind their manners—
everybody was always good-mannered where he was. Everybody loved to have him around, too; he was sunshine most
always—I mean he made it seem like good weather. When he
turned into a cloud-bank it was awful dark for half a minute,
and that was enough; there wouldn't nothing go wrong again
for a week.

When him and the old lady come down in the morning
all the family got up out of their chairs and give them good
day, and didn't set down again till they had set down. Then
Tom and Bob went to the sideboard where the decanters was
and mixed a glass of bitters and handed it to him, and he
held it in his hand and waited till Tom's and Bob's was mixed,
and then they bowed and said, "Our duty to you, sir, and
madam," and *they* bowed the least bit in the world and said
thank you, and so they drank, all three, and Bob and Tom
poured a spoonful of water on the sugar and the mite of
whisky or apple-brandy in the bottom of their tumblers and
give it to me and Buck, and we drank to the old people too.

Bob was the oldest and Tom next—tall, beautiful men with
very broad shoulders and brown faces, and long black hair
and black eyes. They dressed in white linen from head to foot,
like the old gentleman, and wore broad Panama hats.

Then there was Miss Charlotte; she was twenty-five and
tall and proud and grand but as good as she could be when
she warn't stirred up, but when she was she had a look that
would make you wilt in your tracks, like her father. She was
beautiful.

So was her sister, Miss Sophia, but it was a different kind.
She was gentle and sweet like a dove and she was only twenty.

Each person had their own nigger to wait on them—Buck too. My nigger had a monstrous easy time, because I warn't used to having anybody do anything for me, but Buck's was on the jump most of the time.

This was all there was of the family now, but there used to be more—three sons; they got killed; and Emmeline that died.

The old gentleman owned a lot of farms and over a hundred niggers. Sometimes a stack of people would come there, horseback, from ten or fifteen mile around, and stay five or six days and have such junketings round about and on the river, and dances and picnics in the woods daytimes, and balls at the house nights. These people was mostly kinfolks of the family. The men brought their guns with them. It was a handsome lot of quality, I tell you.

There was another clan of aristocracy around there—five or six families—mostly of the name of Shepherdson. They was as high-toned and well born and rich and grand as the tribe of Grangerfords. The Shepherdsons and Grangerfords used the same steamboat landing, which was about two mile above our house; so sometimes when I went up there with a lot of our folks I used to see a lot of the Shepherdsons there on their fine horses.

One day Buck and me was away out in the woods hunting and heard a horse coming. We was crossing the road. Buck says:

"Quick! Jump for the woods!"

We done it, and then peeped down the woods through the leaves. Pretty soon a splendid young man come galloping down the road, setting his horse easy and looking like a soldier. He had his gun across his pommel. I had seen him before. It was young Harney Shepherdson. I heard Buck's gun go off at my ear, and Harney's hat tumbled off from his head. He grabbed his gun and rode straight to the place where we was hid. But we didn't wait. We started through the woods on a run. The woods warn't thick, so I looked over my shoulder to dodge the bullet, and twice I seen Harney cover Buck with his gun; and then he rode away the way he come—to get his hat, I reckon, but I couldn't see. We never stopped running till we got home. The old gentleman's eyes blazed a minute— 'twas pleasure, mainly, I judged—then his face sort of smoothed down, and he says, kind of gentle:

"I don't like that shooting from behind a bush. Why didn't you step into the road, my boy?"

"The Shepherdsons don't, father. They always take advantage."

Miss Charlotte she held her head up like a queen while Buck was telling his tale, and her nostrils spread and her eyes snapped. The two young men looked dark but never said nothing. Miss Sophia she turned pale, but the color come back when she found the man warn't hurt.

Soon as I could get Buck down by the corn-cribs under the trees by ourselves, I says:

"Did you want to kill him, Buck?"

"Well, I bet I did."

"What did he do to you?"

"Him? He never done nothing to me."

"Well, then, what did you want to kill him for?"

"Why, nothing—only it's on account of the feud."

"What's a feud?"

"Why, where was you raised? Don't you know what a feud is?"

"Never heard of it before—tell me about it."

"Well," says Buck, "a feud is this way: A man has a quarrel with another man, and kills him; then that other man's brother kills *him;* then the other brothers on both sides goes for one another; then the *cousins* chip in—and by and by everybody's killed off and there ain't no more feud. But it's kind of slow and takes a long time."

"Has this one been going on long, Buck?"

"Well, I should *reckon*! It started thirty year ago, or som'ers along there. There was trouble 'bout something and then a lawsuit to settle it, and the suit went agin one of the men and so he up and shot the man that won the suit—which he would naturally do, of course. Anybody would."

"What was the trouble about, Buck?—land?"

"I reckon maybe—I don't know."

"Well, who done the shooting? Was it a Grangerford or a Shepherdson?"

"Laws, how do *I* know? It was so long ago."

"Don't anybody know?"

"Oh, yes, pa knows, I reckon, and some of the other old people; but they don't know now what the row was about in the first place."

"Has there been many killed, Buck?"

"Yes; right smart chance of funerals. But they don't always kill. Pa's got a few buckshot in him, but he don't mind it 'cuz he don't weigh much, anyway. Bob's been carved up some with a bowie and Tom's been hurt once or twice."

"Has anybody been killed this year, Buck?"

"Yes; we got one and they got one. 'Bout three months ago my cousin Bud, fourteen year old, was riding through the woods on t'other side of the river and didn't have no weapon with him, which was blame' foolishness, and in a lonesome place he hears a horse a-coming behind him and sees old Baldy Shepherdson a-linkin' after him with his gun in his hand and his white hair a-flying in the wind; and 'stead of jumping off and taking to the brush, Bud 'lowed he could outrun him; so they had it nip and tuck for five mile or more, the old man a-gaining all the time; so at last Bud seen it warn't any use, so he stopped and faced around so as to have the bullet holes in front, you know, and the old man he rode up and shot him down. But he didn't git much chance to enjoy his luck, for inside of a week our folks laid *him* out."

"I reckon that old man was a coward, Buck."

"I reckon he *warn't* a coward. Not by a blame' sight. There ain't a coward amongst them Shepherdsons—not a one. And there ain't no cowards amongst the Grangerfords either. Why, that old man kep' up his end in a fight one day for half an hour against three Grangerfords, and come out winner. They was all a-horseback; he lit off of his horse and got behind a little woodpile and kep' his horse before him to stop the bullets; but the Grangerfords stayed on their horses and capered around the old man and peppered away at him, and he peppered away at them. Him and his horse both went home pretty leaky and crippled, but the Grangerfords had to be *fetched* home—and one of 'em was dead and another died the next day. No, sir; if a body's out hunting for cowards he don't want to fool away any time amongst them Shepherdsons, becuz they don't breed any of that *kind.*"

Next Sunday we all went to church, about three mile, everybody a-horseback. The men took their guns along, so did Buck, and kept them between their knees or stood them handy against the wall. The Shepherdsons done the same. It was pretty ornery preaching—all about brotherly love, and such-like tiresomeness; but everybody said it was a good sermon and they all talked it over going home, and had such a powerful lot to say about faith and good works and free grace and preforeordestination, and I don't know what all, that it did seem to me to be one of the roughest Sundays I had run across yet.

About an hour after dinner everybody was dozing around, some in their chairs and some in their rooms, and it got to be pretty dull. Buck and a dog was stretched out on the grass in the sun sound asleep. I went up to our room, and judged I would take a nap myself. I found that sweet Miss Sophia standing in her door, which was next to ours, and she took me in her room and shut the door very soft and asked me if I liked her, and I said I did; and she asked me if I would do something for her and not tell anybody, and I said I would. Then she said she'd forgot her Testament and left it in the seat at church between two other books, and would I slip out quiet and go there and fetch it to her and not say nothing to nobody. I said I would. So I slid out and slipped off up the road and there warn't anybody at the church, except maybe a hog or two, for there warn't any lock on the door, and hogs likes a puncheon floor in summer-time because it's cool. If you notice, most folks don't go to church only when they've got to; but a hog is different.

Says I to myself, something's up; it ain't natural for a girl to be in such a sweat about a Testament. So I give it a shake, and out drops a little piece of paper with *"Half past two"* wrote on it with a pencil. I ransacked it, but couldn't find anything else. I couldn't make anything out of that, so I put the paper in the book again, and when I got home and upstairs there was Miss Sophia in her door waiting for me. She pulled me in and shut the door; then she looked in the Testament till she found the paper, and as soon as she read it she looked glad; and before a body could think she grabbed me and give me a squeeze, and said I was the best boy in the world, and not to tell anybody. She was mighty red in the face for a minute and her eyes lighted up, and it made her powerful pretty. I was a good deal astonished but when I got my breath I asked her what the paper was about, and she asked me if I had read it, and I said no, and she asked me if I could read writing, and I told her "no, only coarse-hand," and then she said the paper warn't

anything but a book-mark to keep her pla͡
and play now.

I went off down to the river, studyin͞
pretty soon I noticed that my nigg͡
behind. When we was out of sight of the h͡
and around a second and then comes a-running, ͡

"Mars Jawge, if you'll come down into de swamp ͞
you a whole stack o' water-moccasins."

Thinks I, that's mighty curious; he said that yesterday. He oughter know a body don't love water-moccasins enough to go around hunting for them. What is he up to, anyway? So I says:

"All right; trot ahead."

I followed a half a mile; then he struck out over the swamp and waded ankle-deep as much as another half-mile. We come to a little flat piece of land which was dry and very thick with trees and bushes and vines, and he says:

"You shove right in dah jist a few steps, Mars Jawge; dah's whah dey is. I's seed 'em befo'; I don't k'yer to see 'em no mo'."

Then he slopped right along and went away, and pretty soon the trees hid him. I poked into the place a ways and come to a little open patch as big as a bedroom all hung around with vines, and found a man laying there asleep—and, by jings, it was my old Jim!

I waked him up and I reckoned it was going to be a grand surprise to him to see me again, but it warn't. He nearly cried he was so glad, but he warn't surprised. Said he swum along behind me that night, and heard me yell every time, but dasn't answer, because he didn't want nobody to pick *him* up and take him into slavery again. Says he:

"I got hurt a little, en couldn't swim fas', so I wuz a considerable ways behine you towards de las'; when you landed I reck'ned I could ketch up wid you on de lan' 'dout havin' to

ut at you, but when I see dat house I begin to go slow. I
z off too fur to hear what dey say to you—I wuz 'fraid o'
de dogs; but when it 'uz all quiet agin I knowed you's in de
house, so I struck out for de woods to wait for day. Early in
de mawnin' some er de niggers come along, gwyne to de
fields, en dey tuck me en showed me dis place, whah de dogs
can't track me on accounts o' de water, en dey brings me truck
to eat every night, en tells me how you's a-gittin' along."

"Why didn't you tell my Jack to fetch me here sooner,
Jim?"

"Well, 'twarn't no use to 'sturb you, Huck, tell we could
do sumfn—but we's all right now. I ben a-buyin' pots en pans
en vittles, as I got a chanst, en a-patchin' up de raf' nights
when—"

"*What* raft, Jim?"

"Our ole raf'."

"You mean to say our old raft warn't smashed all to
flinders?"

"No, she warn't. She was tore up a good deal—one en' of
her was; but dey warn't no great harm done, on'y our traps
was mos' all los'. Ef we hadn' dive' so deep en swum so fur
under water, en de night hadn' ben so dark, en we warn't so
sk'yerd, en ben sich punkin-heads, as de sayin' is, we'd a seed
de raf'. But it's jis' as well we didn't, 'kase now she's all fixed
up agin mos' as good as new, en we's got a new lot o' stuff,
too, in de place o' what 'uz los'."

"Why, how did you get hold of the raft again, Jim—did
you catch her?"

"How I gwyne to ketch her en I out in de woods? No;
some er de niggers foun' her ketched on a snag along heah in
de ben', en dey hid her in a crick 'mongst de willows, en dey
wuz so much jawin' 'bout which un 'um she b'long to de mos'
dat I come to heah 'bout it pooty soon, so I ups en settles de

trouble by tellin' 'um she don't b'long to none uv 'um, but to you en me; en I ast 'm if dey gwyne to grab a young white genlman's propaty, en git a hid'n' for it? Den I gin 'm ten cents apiece, en dey 'uz mighty well satisfied, en wisht some mo' raf's 'ud come along en make 'm rich agin. Dey's mighty good to me, dese niggers is, en whatever I wants 'm to do fur me I doan' have to ast 'm twice, honey. Dat Jack's a good nigger, en pooty smart."

"Yes, he is. He ain't ever told me you was here; told me to come and he'd show me a lot of water-moccasins. If anything happens *he* ain't mixed up in it. He can say he never seen us together, and it'll be the truth."

I don't want to talk much about the next day. I reckon I'll cut it pretty short. I waked up about dawn and was a-going to turn over and go to sleep again when I noticed how still it was—didn't seem to be anybody stirring. That warn't usual. Next I noticed that Buck was up and gone. Well, I gets up, a-wondering, and goes downstairs—nobody around; everything as still as a mouse. Just the same outside. Thinks I, what does it mean? Down by the woodpile I comes across my Jack, and says:

"What's it all about?"

Says he:

"Don't you know, Mars Jawge?"

"No," says I, "I don't."

"Well, den, Miss Sophia's run off! 'deed she has. She run off in de night some time—nobody don't know jis' when; run off to get married to dat young Harney Shepherdson, you know—leastways, so dey 'spec. De fambly foun' it out 'bout half an hour ago—maybe a little mo'—en' I *tell* you dey warn't no time los'. Sich another hurryin' up guns en hosses *you* never see! De women folks has gone for to stir up de relations, en ole Mars Saul en de boys tuck dey guns en rode up de river road for to try to ketch dat young man en kill him 'fo' he kin git acrost de river wid Miss Sophia. I reck'n dey's gwyne to be mighty rough times."

"Buck went off 'thout waking me up."

"Well, I reck'n he *did*! Dey warn't gwyne to mix you up in it. Mars Buck he loaded up his gun en 'lowed he's gwyne to fetch home a Shepherdson or bust. Well, dey'll be plenty un 'm dah, I reck'n, en you bet you he'll fetch one ef he gits a chanst."

I took up the river road as hard as I could put. By and by I begin to hear guns a good ways off. When I come in sight of the log store and the woodpile where the steamboats lands I worked along under the trees and brush till I got to a good place, and then I clumb up into the forks of a cottonwood that was out of reach, and watched. There was a wood-rank four foot high a little ways in front of the tree, and first I was going to hide behind that; but maybe it was luckier I didn't.

There was four or five men cavorting around on their horses in the open place before the log store, cussing and yelling and trying to get at a couple of young chaps that was behind the wood-rank alongside of the steamboat landing, but they couldn't come it. Every time one of them showed himself on the river side of the woodpile he got shot at. The two boys was squatting back to back behind the pile, so they could watch both ways.

By and by the men stopped cavorting around and yelling. They started riding towards the store; then up gets one of the boys, draws a steady bead over the wood-rank, and drops one of them out of his saddle. All the men jumped off of their horses and grabbed the hurt one and started to carry him to the store; and that minute the two boys started on the run. They got halfway to the tree I was in before the men noticed. Then the men see them and jumped on their horses and took out after them. They gained on the boys but it didn't do no good, the boys had too good a start; they got to the woodpile that was in front of my tree and slipped in behind it, and so they had the bulge on the men again. One of the boys was Buck, and the other was a slim young chap about nineteen years old.

The men ripped around awhile and then rode away. As soon as they was out of sight I sung out to Buck and told him. He didn't know what to make of my voice coming out of the tree at first. He was awful surprised. He told me to watch out sharp and let him know when the men come in sight again; said they was up to some devilment or other—wouldn't be gone long. I wished I was out of that tree but I dasn't come down. Buck begun to cry and rip, and 'lowed that him and his cousin Joe (that was the other young chap) would make up for this day yet. He said his father and his two brothers was killed, and two or three of the enemy. Said the Shepherdsons laid for them in ambush. Buck said his father and brothers ought to waited for their relations—the Shepherdsons was too strong for them. I asked him what was become of young Harney and Miss Sophia. He said they'd got across the river and was safe. I was glad of that, but the way Buck did take on because he didn't manage to kill Harney that day he shot at him—I hain't ever heard anything like it.

All of a sudden, bang! bang! bang! goes three or four guns—the men had slipped around through the woods and come in from behind without their horses! The boys jumped for the river—both of them hurt—and as they swum down the current the men run along the bank shooting at them and singing out, "Kill them, kill them!" It made me so sick I most fell out of the tree. I ain't a-going to tell *all* that happened— it would make me sick again if I was to do that. I wished I hadn't ever come ashore that night to see such things. I ain't ever going to get shut of them—lots of times I dream about them.

I stayed in the tree till it begun to get dark, afraid to come down. Sometimes I heard guns away off in the woods and twice I seen little gangs of men gallop past the log store with guns; so I reckoned the trouble was still a-going on. I was mighty downhearted; so I made up my mind I wouldn't ever go anear that house again, because I reckoned I was to blame, somehow. I judged that that piece of paper meant that Miss Sophia was to meet Harney somewheres at half past two and run off, and I judged I ought to told her father about that paper and the curious way she acted, and then maybe he would 'a' locked her up and this awful mess wouldn't ever happened.

When I got down out of the tree I crept along down the riverbank a piece, and found the two bodies laying in the edge of the water, and tugged at them till I got them ashore; then I covered up their faces and got away as quick as I could. I cried a little when I was covering up Buck's face, for he was mighty good to me.

It was just dark now. I never went near the house but struck through the woods and made for the swamp. Jim warn't on his island, so I tramped off in a hurry for the crick, and crowded through the willows, red-hot to jump aboard and get out of that awful country. The raft was gone! My souls, but I was scared! I couldn't get my breath for most a minute. Then I raised a yell. A voice not twenty-five foot from me says:

"Good lan'! is dat you, honey? Doan' make no noise."

It was Jim's voice—nothing ever sounded so good before. I run along the bank a piece and got aboard and Jim he grabbed me and hugged me, he was so glad to see me. He says:

"Laws bless you, chile, I 'uz right down sho' you's dead agin. Jack's been heah; he say he reck'n you's ben shot, kase you didn' come home no mo'; so I's jes' dis minute a-startin' de raf' down towards de mouf er de crick, so's to be all ready for to shove out en leave soon as Jack comes agin en tells me for certain you *is* dead. Lawsy, I's mighty glad to git you back agin, honey."

I says:

"All right—that's mighty good; they won't find me, and they'll think I've been killed, and floated down the river—there's something up there that'll help them think so—so don't you lose no time, Jim, but just shove off for the big water as fast as ever you can."

I never felt easy till the raft was two mile below there and out in the middle of the Mississippi. Then we hung up our signal lantern and judged that we was free and safe once more. I hadn't had a bite to eat since yesterday, so Jim he got out some corn-dodgers and buttermilk, and pork and cabbage and greens—there ain't nothing in the world so good when it's cooked right—and whilst I eat my supper we talked and had a good time. I was powerful glad to get away from the feuds, and so was Jim to get away from the swamp. We said there warn't no home like a raft, after all. Other places do seem so cramped up and smothery, but a raft don't. You feel mighty free and easy and comfortable on a raft.

ACKNOWLEDGMENTS

All possible care has been taken to trace ownership and secure permission for each selection in this series. The Great Books Foundation wishes to thank the following authors, publishers, and representatives for permission to reprint copyrighted material:

Sucker, from COLLECTED STORIES OF CARSON MCCULLERS. Copyright 1987 by Floria V. Lasky, Executrix of the Estate of Carson McCullers. Reprinted by permission of Houghton Mifflin Company.

The Summer of the Beautiful White Horse, from MY NAME IS ARAM, by William Saroyan. Copyright 1939 by William Saroyan; renewed 1966 by William Saroyan. Reprinted by permission of Harcourt Brace Jovanovich, Inc.

Rules of the Game, from THE JOY LUCK CLUB, by Amy Tan. Copyright 1989 by Amy Tan. Reprinted by permission of Putnam Publishing Group.

The Destructors, from COLLECTED STORIES, by Graham Greene. Copyright 1955, 1983 by Graham Greene. Reprinted by permission of Viking Penguin, a division of Penguin Books USA, Inc.

The Watch, from THREE NOVELLAS, by Ivan Turgenev. Translation copyright 1968 by Marion Mainwaring. Reprinted by permission of Georges Borchardt, Inc.

Approximations, from ANYWHERE BUT HERE, by Mona Simpson. Copyright 1986 by Mona Simpson. Reprinted by permission of Alfred A. Knopf, Inc.

Star Food, from EMPEROR OF THE AIR, by Ethan Canin. Copyright 1988 by Ethan Canin. Reprinted by permission of Houghton Mifflin Company.

Winter, from THE WINTER ROOM, by Gary Paulsen. Copyright 1989 by Gary Paulsen. Reprinted by permission of Orchard Books.

High School Graduation, from I KNOW WHY THE CAGED BIRD SINGS, by Maya Angelou. Copyright 1969 by Maya Angelou. Reprinted by permission of Random House, Inc.

Cover art by Ed Young. Copyright 1992 by Ed Young.

Text and cover design by William Seabright, William Seabright & Associates.